Key Stage 3
Developing Numeracy

MEASURES, SHAPE AND SPACE

ACTIVITIES FOR TEACHING NUMERACY

year 7

Hilary Koll and Steve Mills

A & C BLACK

Contents

Geometrical reasoning: lines, angles and shapes

Transformations

Coordinates

Construction

Measures and mensuration

Answers

Published 2004 by A & C Black Publishers Limited
37 Soho Square, London W1D 3QZ
www.acblack.com

ISBN 0-7136-6474-6

The authors and publishers would like to thank David Chadwick, Corinne McCrum and Jane McNeill for their advice in producing this series of books.

A CIP catalogue record for this book is available from the British Library.

Printed in Great Britain by Caligraving Ltd, Thetford, Norfolk.

A & C Black uses paper produced with elemental chlorine-free pulp, harvested from managed sustainable forests.

Introduction

Key Stage 3 Developing Numeracy: Measures, Shape and Space is a series of photocopiable resources for Years 7, 8 and 9, designed to be used during maths lessons. The books focus on the Shape, Space and Measures strand of the Key Stage 3 National Strategy *Framework for teaching mathematics*.

Each book supports the teaching of mathematics by providing a series of activities that develop essential skills in numeracy. The activities aim to reinforce learning and develop the skills and understanding explored during whole-class teaching. Each task provides practice and consolidation of an objective contained in the framework document. On the whole the activities are designed for pupils to work on independently, either individually or in pairs, although occasionally some pupils may need support.

The activities in **Measures, Shape and Space Year 7** relate to the following topics:
- geometrical reasoning: lines, angles and shapes;
- transformations;
- coordinates;
- construction;
- measures and mensuration.

How to use this book

Each double-page spread is based on a Year 7 objective. The spread has three main sections labelled A, B and C, and ends with a challenge (**Now try this!**). The work grows increasingly difficult from A through to C, and the 'Now try this!' challenge reinforces and extends pupils' learning. The activities provide the teacher with an opportunity to make informal assessments: for example, checking that pupils are developing mental strategies, have grasped the main teaching points, or whether they have any misunderstandings.

This double-page structure can be used in a variety of ways: for example, following whole-class teaching the pupils can begin to work through both sheets and will experience gradually more complex questions, or the teacher can choose the most appropriate starting points for each group in the class, with some pupils starting at A and others at B or C. This allows differentiation for mixed-ability groups. 'Now try this!' provides a greater challenge for more able pupils. It can involve 'Using and Applying' concepts and skills, and provides an opportunity for classroom discussion. Where appropriate, pupils can be asked to finish tasks for homework.

The instructions are presented clearly to enable the pupils to work independently. There are also opportunities for pupils to work in pairs and groups, to encourage discussion and co-operation. A calculator icon indicates whether or not calculators should be used for different parts of the activities. Where there is no icon, the teacher or pupils may choose whether or not to use them. Brief notes are provided at the foot of each page to assist the pupil or classroom assistant, or parent if the sheets are used for homework. Remind the pupils to read these before beginning the activity.

In some cases, the pupils will need to record their workings on a separate piece of paper, and it is suggested that these workings are handed in with the activity sheets. The pupils will also need to record their answers to some of the 'Now try this!' challenges on another piece of paper.

Organisation

Very little equipment is needed, other than rulers, sharp pencils, protractors, pairs of compasses and calculators. The pupils will also need squared paper, dotty paper, thin card, tracing paper, scissors and glue for some of the activities.

To help teachers select appropriate learning experiences for pupils, the activities are grouped into sections within the book to match the objectives in the Key Stage 3 National Strategy *Yearly teaching programmes*. However, the activities do not have to be used in the order given. The sheets are intended to support, rather than direct, the teacher's planning.

Some activities can be made easier or more challenging by masking or substituting some of the numbers. You may wish to re-use some pages by copying them onto card and laminating them, or by enlarging them onto A3 paper. They could also be made into OHTs for whole-class use.

Teachers' notes

Further brief notes, containing specific instructions or points to be raised during the first part of the lesson, are provided for particular sheets (see pages 6–7).

Whole-class oral and mental starters

The following activities provide some practical ideas to support the main teaching part of the lesson, and can be carried out before the pupils use the activity sheets.

Geometrical reasoning: lines, angles and shapes

Draw it!

Ask a pupil to draw a shape, such as a polygon or compound shape, at a particular orientation and position on a sheet of paper. The pupil should then come to the front and describe the shape as fully as possible to the rest of the class with reference to shape, orientation, angles, position on the paper, and so on. The other pupils attempt to draw the shape. Encourage them to ask questions which may be answered only *yes* or *no*.

Transformations

What's the transformation?

Using stiff card, draw and cut out two identical 'L' shapes made up of five squares, as shown. The colour of the card should be the same on both sides of the shapes.

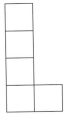

Holding one 'L' shape in each hand with arms outstretched, display the shapes in two different orientations. Ask the pupils to say how one shape has been transformed to the other: for example, a horizontal translation, a rotation through 180 degrees, a reflection.

Coordinates

Quadrant bingo

Ask the pupils to draw a 6 × 6 coordinate grid on squared paper, and to label the axes ⁻3 to +3. Each pupil should mark seven points on the grid with crosses, making sure that each point has whole number coordinates. Call out pairs of coordinates; any pupils whose cross is 'hit' should circle it. The last player with an uncircled cross is the winner. Keep a record of the coordinates so that the winner's grid can be checked. Encourage the pupils to place crosses on the *x*- and *y*-axes (they may otherwise not think of doing this).

Construction

Nets

You need plastic interlocking shapes which can be joined to make nets of 3-D shapes. Interlock several pieces in different ways and ask the pupils to say whether or not each net will fold to make a 3-D shape.

Measures and mensuration

Conversion tables

Make and laminate two simple tables as shown:

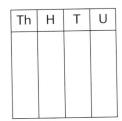 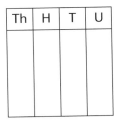

Th	H	T	U

Th	H	T	U

Attach the tables to the board and write two related metric units to the right of the boards, for example *m* and *cm*. Discuss the relationship between the two units. Then write a measurement on one table as shown below, using a wipe-off pen. Ask pupils to come to the front and to fill in the equivalent measurement on the other table:

Th	H	T	U	
			2	m
		5	4	m

Th	H	T	U	
		2	0	0	cm
5	4	0	0	cm

Area match

Draw several different shapes on a large dotty grid, for example:

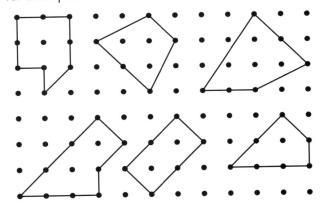

Ask the pupils to calculate the area of each shape by splitting it into squares, rectangles and triangles, and then finding the total. They could be asked to match any shapes with the same area or, on their own piece of dotty paper, to draw other shapes with the same area as a chosen shape.

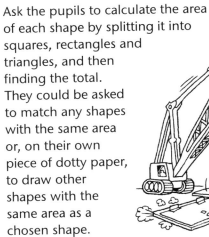

5

Teachers' notes

Geometrical reasoning: lines, angles and shapes

Pages 8 & 9

Begin the lesson by discussing words and conventions of drawing and labelling lines and angles, including labelling vertices of shapes. Revise parallel and perpendicular lines and the symbols for marking parallel lines and lines of equal length. Ask the pupils to give suggestions of where parallel and perpendicular lines might be seen in real life (for example, the two opposite edges of a door are parallel; the lines at the corner of a rectangular window are perpendicular). Also revise names and properties of shapes, in particular parallelogram and isosceles triangle.

Pages 10 & 11

Revise angles created by sets of parallel, perpendicular and intersecting lines by drawing and labelling lines and several angles on the board. Invite pupils to come to the front and to mark other angles that can be found from the information given.

Pages 12 & 13

The pupils will need scissors and tracing paper (or thin paper) to trace and cut out the shapes in part A. Alternatively, they could construct these shapes themselves using a ruler and a protractor. Encourage the pupils to notice that the three shapes can be arranged to make a square. In part C, explain that the shapes in each diagram are congruent: for example, in question (b) the two triangles are identical and the two parallelograms are identical.

Pages 14 & 15

These pages provide opportunities for the pupils to visualise 2-D shapes. Initially, discourage any drawing of shapes and ask the pupils to hold the image of the shape in their head. Further questions can be asked about the symmetries, diagonals and angles of the shapes visualised.

Pages 16 & 17

It may be useful to revise the definitions and properties of triangles, quadrilaterals and regular polygons before the pupils tackle these pages. In part A, encourage the pupils to draw examples which fit only into the specified category of shape: for example, they should not draw a rhombus or rectangle as a type of trapezium.

Pages 18 & 19

The pupils will find it helpful to make the nets by clicking together square plastic construction materials. They will need thin card and scissors for part B. In part C, they could be given a dice or cubes to examine.

Transformations

Pages 20 & 21

Discuss the convention of showing the vertices of an image using A' as the image of A, B' as the image of B, and so on. The pupils could be given small mirrors or reflecting equipment to help them complete the activity and to check their work.

Pages 22 & 23

The pupils could be given small mirrors or reflecting equipment to help them complete the activity and to check their work. In part C, each pair will need a dice, two counters and two different-coloured pens. Squared paper will be needed for the 'Now try this!' challenge.

Pages 24 & 25

Provide the pupils with tracing paper to help them complete the activity and to check their rotations. They should examine the images they create in part B and notice that they are all at the same orientation, but in a different position in relation to the original shape. Encourage them to use this fact when checking other rotations that they draw. Squared paper and coloured pencils will be needed for the 'Now try this!' challenge.

Pages 26 & 27

Provide the pupils with tracing paper to help them complete the activity and to check their answers. They will require squared paper for the 'Now try this!' challenge.

Pages 28 & 29

Scissors and card will be needed for the 'Now try this!' challenge. If appropriate, introduce the pupils to other ways of writing and recording translations. Rather than saying 3 units left and 2 units up, show this as $(-3, 2)$ or using the vertical representation: $\begin{pmatrix} -3 \\ 2 \end{pmatrix}$

Pages 30 & 31

For part C, each pupil will need coloured pencils in five different shades.

Coordinates

Pages 32 & 33

During the first part of the lesson, revise coordinates in each of the four quadrants and discuss phrases which will help the pupils with coordinates: for example, *Along the corridor and up or down the stairs* and *x is a cross (across), y is high.*

Introduce the names for the quadrants from first to fourth, and ensure that the pupils appreciate whether the *x*- and *y*-coordinates are positive or negative for points in each quadrant.

Pages 34 & 35

In part C, the pupils will need a good understanding of the names and properties of quadrilaterals. This could be revised by drawing a grid on the board and asking pupils to mark points as the vertices of different types of quadrilaterals. Invite other pupils to give the coordinates of the vertices, and discuss the properties of the shapes.

Construction

Pages 36 & 37

Ensure that the pupils have suitable rulers marked in millimetres. Discuss the different ways of recording a small measurement (for example, 3.2 cm, 32 mm or 3 cm and 2 mm). As a starter activity in the first part of the lesson, call out a measurement in one of these forms and ask the pupils to give it using a different unit or form.

Pages 38 & 39

The pupils will need protractors for this activity. Begin the lesson by demonstrating how to use a protractor when measuring angles in different orientations. You could draw several angles on the board and ask the pupils to hold their protractors up to indicate the correct orientation for measuring each angle.

Pages 40 & 41

The pupils will need a ruler marked in millimetres and a protractor. In part C, each pair will require a sheet of A3 paper.

Pages 42 & 43

These pages provide opportunities for the pupils to explore nets and construct them accurately. They will need thin card and scissors to enable them to construct the nets and fold them to make 3-D shapes. Also discuss how to add tabs on alternate edges of the net so that they can be glued together.

Measures and mensuration

Pages 44 & 45

For part C, you need to collect a range of items such as a mug, ruler, calculator, rubbish bin, shampoo bottle, teapot, video cassette, hole-punch, and so on. Ask the pupils to work in groups and to estimate the length, mass or capacity of each item, giving the highest and lowest values they think the measurement will lie between. Once all the estimates have been made, ask each group to give their range. Then measure the item; all groups whose range includes the value score 1 point. The group with the smallest range (if correct) scores a further 3 points.

Pages 46 & 47

The pupils may need help to understand how the table in part C works. Sketch a similar table on the board and discuss the number of each unit that makes up another (for example, how many centimetres make one metre, or what fraction of a metre is one millimetre). Demonstrate how the table can be used to show equivalent measurements by filling in digits and asking the pupils to say the measurement in different units (for example, 42 mm is 0.042 m).

Pages 48 & 49

Revise the terms 'capacity', 'mass', 'area' and 'diameter', and ask the pupils to suggest possible metric units that could be used to measure each one.

Pages 50 & 51

For part C and the 'Now try this!' challenge, revise how to find the area of a right-angled triangle and a parallelogram. The pupils could create their own patterns by rotating shapes and finding the areas and perimeters of the patterns. These could be made into a display which can be used as a visual stimulus for other lessons and as a reminder to pupils of how to find areas and perimeters of compound shapes.

Pages 52 & 53

Before the pupils tackle these pages, revise the definitions of acute, right, obtuse, straight and reflex angles.

Pages 54 & 55

As a further investigation, once part C has been completed, the pupils could explore Pick's Theorem. This states that the area of a shape on a square dotty grid can be found by counting the number of dots along the perimeter (*d*) and the number of dots inside the shape (*i*) and using the formula:

Area = $(\frac{1}{2}d + i) - 1$

Pick's Theorem can be used to check the answers to all the areas in part C and to the 'Now try this!' challenge.

Pages 58 & 59

In question C1, to ensure pupils do not show the same cuboids in different orientations, first ask pupils to come to the board and to sketch the cuboid shown on the page in different orientations. Explain that these are congruent shapes (they are identical but in a different orientation). Stress that the cuboids should all have different dimensions.

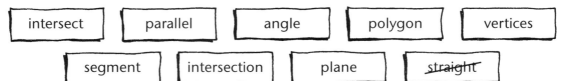

What's the convention?

1. Write the correct missing word in each space.

| intersect | parallel | angle | polygon | vertices |

| segment | intersection | plane | ~~straight~~ |

When two ___*straight*___ lines cross at a point, they are said to

_____.

The point at which they cross is called the _____.

A line with end-points A and B is called the line _____ AB.

When two lines are ┃equidistant┃ and never cross they are called

_____ lines.

When two line segments meet at a point, the measure of rotation of one of the lines segments to the other is called the _____.

A _____ is a 2-D shape made from line segments on the same flat surface (_____).

The line segments are called the sides. The end-points of these sides are called _____.

2. Discuss your answers with a partner.

B

Here are the conventions for labelling triangles:

☆ The vertices are labelled using capital letters, going round in order (clockwise or anticlockwise).

☆ The corresponding lower-case letter is given to the side opposite each vertex.

ALIEN CONVENTION 2099

Tick the triangles below which are labelled correctly.

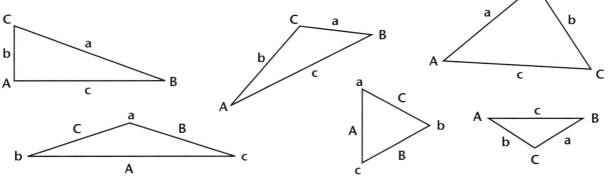

 Use a maths dictionary to find the meanings of any words of which you are unsure. **Equidistant** lines are the same distance apart all along their length.

Developing Numeracy
Measures, Shape and Space
Year 7
© A & C BLACK

C 1. Look at these diagrams.

Make sure you know the meaning of the symbols along the edges of the shapes.

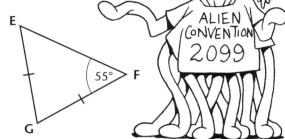

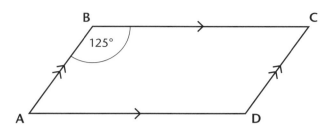

Write whether each statement is true or false.

(a) AD is parallel to BC ___true___

(b) EF is equal in length to FG _____

(c) EF is | perpendicular | to FG _____

(d) AB = BC _____

(e) AB = CD _____

(f) AB//CD _____

(g) GF//GE _____

(h) ∠EFG = 70° _____

(i) ∠ABC = 125° _____

(j) DÂB = 125° _____

(k) ∠EFG = ∠FGE _____

(l) GÊF = 55° _____

(m) ∆EFG is an isosceles triangle _____

(n) ABCD is a parallelogram _____

> Symbols:
> // is parallel to
> ∠ angle
> ^ angle
> ∆ triangle

!

2. Follow these instructions.

> ☆ Draw and label a triangle XYZ so that XY = XZ and YZ ≠ XZ.
> ☆ Measure the line XZ. Mark the mid-point of XZ halfway along the line. Label this point M.
> ☆ Draw the straight line YM.

(a) Is YM perpendicular to XZ?   Yes ☐   No ☐

Explain how you can be sure of this. _____

_____

(b) Is ∠XYZ equal to ∠YZX?   Yes ☐   No ☐

Explain how you can be sure of this. _____

_____

NOW TRY THIS!

● Draw a rectangle that is not a square. Label the vertices PQRS. Draw the diagonals PR and QS. Label M the point where these two diagonals intersect.

(a) Is ∠PMQ a right angle? _____

(b) Is PM of equal length to MQ? _____

Explain your answers.

 When an angle of a shape is given using the ∠ sign (for example, ∠ABC), the order of the letters is important. The middle letter is the vertex at which the angle is: for example, ∠ABC is the angle at B formed by the line AB touching the line BC. **Perpendicular** means 'at right angles to'. Use a maths dictionary to find the meanings of any words you are unsure of.

Developing Numeracy
Measures, Shape and Space
Year 7
© A & C BLACK

9

Angle tangle

Developing Numeracy
Measures, Shape and Space
Year 7
© A & C BLACK

A 1. Write these capital letters in the correct regions of the Venn diagram.

~~A~~ ~~E~~ F H I J K L M N T V W X Y ~~Z~~

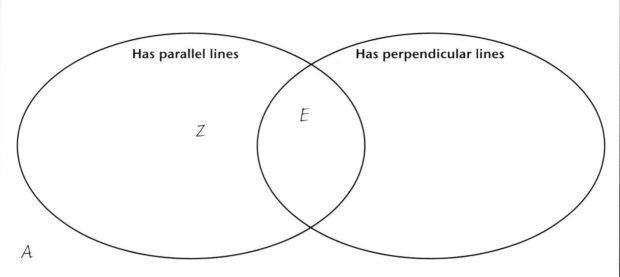

Has parallel lines   Has perpendicular lines

Z   E

A

2. What does this diagram show you about the angles in a triangle and along a straight line?
Discuss it with a partner.

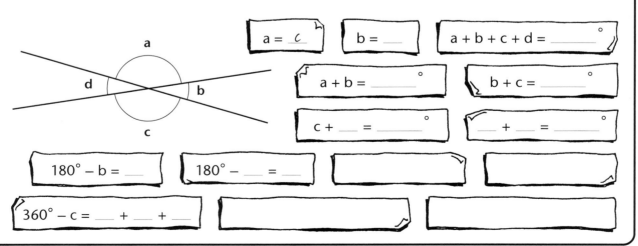

B Complete these facts about the angles in this diagram. Write any more facts you can find.

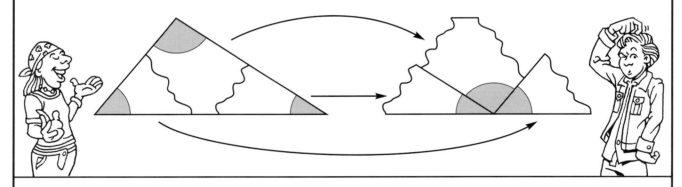

a = _c_   b = ___   a + b + c + d = _____°

a + b = _____°   b + c = _____°

c + ___ = _____°   ___ + ___ = _____°

180° − b = ___   180° − ___ = ___

360° − c = ___ + ___ + ___

Parallel lines are equidistant (always the same distance apart) and can
never cross, however far the lines are extended. **Perpendicular** lines are
at right angles to each other. Remember, angles that meet at a point have
a sum of 360°, and angles that join to make a straight line have a sum
of 180°.

Angle tangle

C Look carefully at this diagram. It shows the rectangle ABCD and some lines drawn inside it. Triangle PQR is a right-angled triangle. Line AS is **parallel** to line TP.

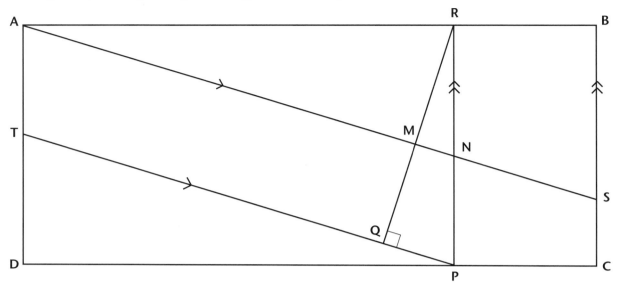

Write whether each statement is true or false.

(a) NS is **perpendicular** to BC _false_

(b) MN is parallel to QP _____

(c) AR is parallel to PC _____

(d) RQ is perpendicular to TP _____

(e) RN is perpendicular to AS _____

(f) PQ is parallel to MN _____

(g) AT is parallel to SC _____

(h) RB is perpendicular to BS _____

(i) AM is perpendicular to TQ _____

(j) RB is parallel to DP _____

(k) AM is parallel to PC _____

(l) AM is perpendicular to RM _____

(m) RP//RQ _____

(n) NS//PC _____

(o) BS//TD _____

(p) MN//TQ _____

(q) $\angle$TQR = 90° _____

(r) $\angle$RPC = 90° _____

(s) $\triangle$RMN is a right-angled triangle _____

(t) $\triangle$TPD is a right-angled triangle _____

> Symbols:
> // is parallel to
> $\angle$ angle
> $\triangle$ triangle

NOW TRY THIS!

● Read the facts about the angles in this diagram. Write at least eighteen more facts about the relationships between the angles.

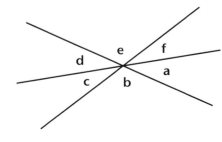

e = b

e + f + a = 180°

Parallel lines are equidistant (always the same distance apart) and can never cross, however far the lines are extended. **Perpendicular** means 'at right angles to'. Remember, angles that meet at a point have a sum of 360°, and angles that join to make a straight line have a sum of 180°.

Developing Numeracy
Measures, Shape and Space
Year 7
© A & C BLACK

From all angles

A

(a) Trace these three shapes and cut them out carefully. Label the angles as shown.

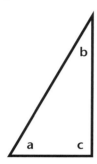

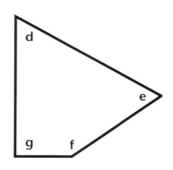

(b) Join the shapes, placing angles together to make right angles and straight lines. Write as many statements as you can showing angles with a total of 90°, 180° or 360°.

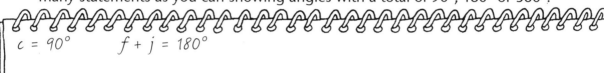

$c = 90°$ $f + j = 180°$

B Find the missing angles in these **isosceles triangles**.

(a)

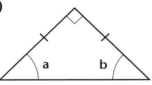

(b)

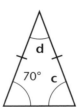

(c)

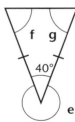

$2a = 180° - 90°$

$a = 45°$

$b = a = 45°$

(d)

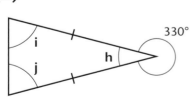

330°

(e)

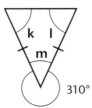

310°

(f)

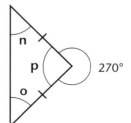

270°

Remember that when angles join to make a straight line, they have a sum of 180°. When angles meet at a point, they have a sum of 360°. An **isosceles triangle** has two equal sides and two equal angles.

Developing Numeracy
Measures, Shape and Space
Year 7
© A & C BLACK

C Each of these patterns is made from shapes. Use the information given to find the missing angles.

(a) three **rhombi**

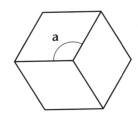

$a = 360° \div 3$

$a = 120°$

(b) two triangles and two parallelograms

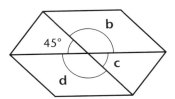

(c) three triangles and three squares

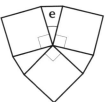

(d) three triangles and three kites

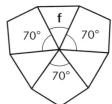

(e) a square and four parallelograms

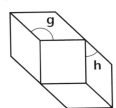

(f) four **equilateral triangles** and four **isosceles triangles**

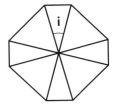

(g) three pentagons and a kite

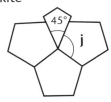

(h) four kites and four rhombi

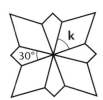

(i) six triangles and six kites

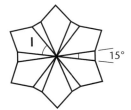

NOW TRY THIS!

- A circle has lines equally spaced which cross at the centre, as shown. What is the angle at the centre between the lines if there are:

(a) 3 lines? _____

(b) 4 lines? _____

(c) 5 lines? _____

(d) 6 lines? _____

3 lines

Remember that when angles meet at a point, they have a sum of 360°.
Rhombi is the plural of rhombus. An **equilateral triangle** has three equal sides and three equal angles of 60°. An **isosceles triangle** has two equal sides and two equal angles.

Developing Numeracy
Measures, Shape and Space
Year 7
© A & C BLACK

Just imagine

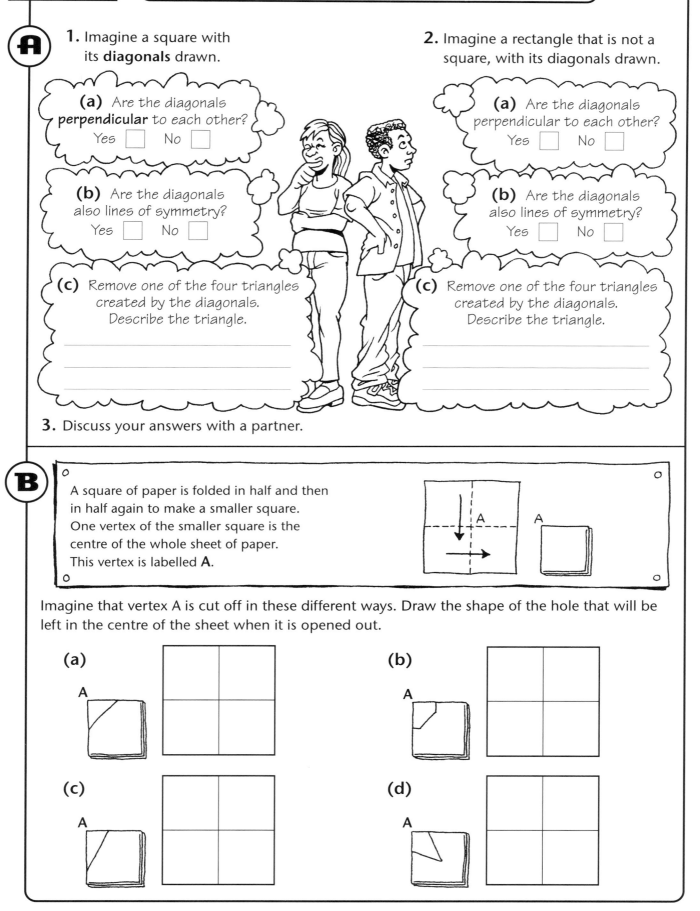

A

1. Imagine a square with its **diagonals** drawn.

(a) Are the diagonals **perpendicular** to each other?
Yes ☐   No ☐

(b) Are the diagonals also lines of symmetry?
Yes ☐   No ☐

(c) Remove one of the four triangles created by the diagonals.
Describe the triangle.

_____
_____
_____

2. Imagine a rectangle that is not a square, with its diagonals drawn.

(a) Are the diagonals perpendicular to each other?
Yes ☐   No ☐

(b) Are the diagonals also lines of symmetry?
Yes ☐   No ☐

(c) Remove one of the four triangles created by the diagonals.
Describe the triangle.

_____
_____
_____

3. Discuss your answers with a partner.

B

A square of paper is folded in half and then in half again to make a smaller square. One vertex of the smaller square is the centre of the whole sheet of paper. This vertex is labelled **A**.

Imagine that vertex A is cut off in these different ways. Draw the shape of the hole that will be left in the centre of the sheet when it is opened out.

(a)

A

(b)

A

(c)

A

(d)

A

  A **diagonal** is a straight line joining two non-adjacent (or opposite) vertices. A square has two diagonals. **Perpendicular** means 'at right angles to'.

14

Just imagine

C 1. Each of these shapes is made from two polygons.
Draw lines to show the joins. One has been done for you.

 The polygons might be **irregular**.
You may need to draw two lines.

(a) [trapezium] and **rhombus** **(b)** square and kite **(c)** trapezium and kite

(d) trapezium and **parallelogram** **(e)** trapezium and trapezium **(f)** rhombus and kite

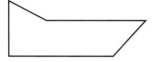 

(g) pentagon and parallelogram **(h)** rectangle and hexagon **(i)** trapezium and trapezium

2. **(a)** Split a square into two polygons in as many different ways as you
can. Only draw one straight line. Name the polygons created.

The polygons do not have to be regular.

(b) Discuss your answers with a partner. How can you be sure that you have found all the
possible pairs of polygons?

NOW TRY THIS! A rhombus and a kite are joined along one or more sides to make a polygon.
- Draw at least six different polygons to match this description.
Show the join between the rhombus and the kite.

 Irregular shapes have unequal sides or angles. A **trapezium** is a
quadrilateral with one pair of parallel sides. It does not have to be
symmetrical. A **parallelogram** has two pairs of parallel sides. A **rhombus** is
a parallelogram with sides of equal length. Remember that a kite can look
like an arrowhead.

Developing Numeracy
Measures, Shape and Space
Year 7
© A & C BLACK   **15**

Shape search

Join three or more dots to make the following shapes.

(a) equilateral triangle

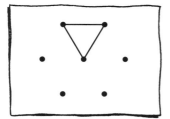

(b) isosceles triangle

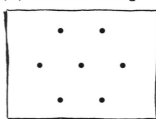

(c) scalene triangle

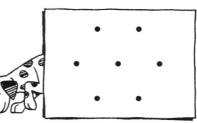

(d) trapezium

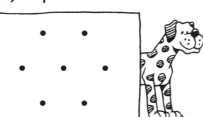

(e) rhombus

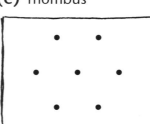

(f) rectangle

(g) kite

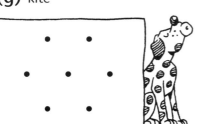

(h) regular hexagon

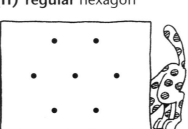

(i) irregular hexagon

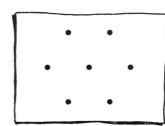

(j) symmetrical pentagon

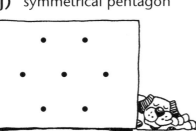

(k) non-symmetrical pentagon

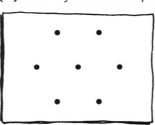

(l) heptagon

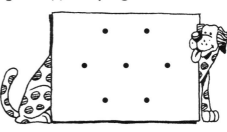

B

1. For the first eight shapes above, list the angles inside each shape.

> Remember, each group of three dots forms an equilateral triangle. Use this to find the angles. **!**

(a) _60°, 60°, 60°_   (b) _____

(c) _____   (d) _____

(e) _____   (f) _____

(g) _____   (h) _____

2. What is the sum of the angles inside:

(a) a triangle? _____   **(b)** a quadrilateral? _____   **(c)** a hexagon? _____

An **equilateral triangle** has three equal sides and three equal angles of 60°. An **isosceles triangle** has two equal sides and two equal angles. The sides and angles of a **scalene triangle** are all different. Remember, a **trapezium** is a quadrilateral with one pair of parallel sides. **Regular** shapes have equal sides and equal angles. A **heptagon** is a polygon with seven sides.

Developing Numeracy
Measures, Shape and Space
Year 7
© A & C BLACK

Shape search

C A rectangle, trapezium and parallelogram are cut into two pieces, as shown (a, b and c). Rearrange the pieces and join them along one edge to make new shapes. Sketch and name the new shapes. Label any lengths you know.

(a) rectangle   *parallelogram*

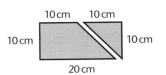   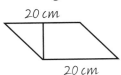

(b) trapezium

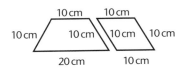

(c) parallelogram

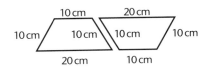

NOW TRY THIS! Pairs of these shapes are joined along one edge.

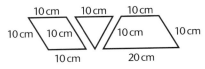

• Tick the shapes which *cannot* be made using two of the shapes above.

☐ rectangle   ☐ **equilateral triangle**   ☐ pentagon

☐ **scalene triangle**   ☐ square   ☐ hexagon

• Explain how you can be sure of your answers. What other shapes can be made?

 When the shapes are joined together, they must join along the length of one edge. You may not be able to give the length of every side. Make as many new shapes as you can for each question. An **equilateral triangle** has three equal sides and three equal angles of 60°. The sides and angles of a **scalene triangle** are all different.

Developing Numeracy
Measures, Shape and Space
Year 7
© A & C BLACK

Cube views

A **1.** Here are three nets that make a cube using six squares. Draw as many other nets as you can that fold to make a cube using six squares.

There are 11 nets in total.

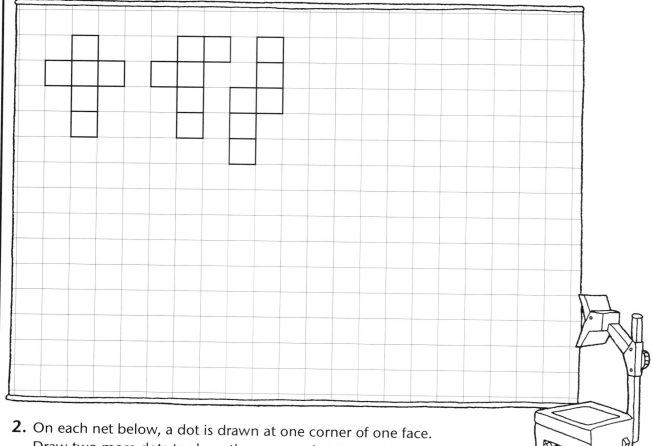

2. On each net below, a dot is drawn at one corner of one face. Draw two more dots to show the corners that join to this dot when the net is folded. The first one has been done for you.

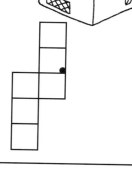

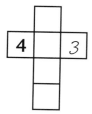 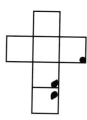 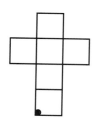 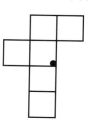 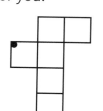

B The numbers on opposite faces of a 1 to 6 dice have a total of 7.

1. Write the numbers 1 to 6 on each net so that opposite faces total 7.

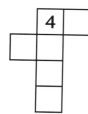 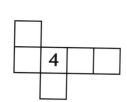 

2. Check your answers by making the nets out of thin card and folding them.

You might find it useful to make these nets by tracing them onto card and cutting them out, or by clicking together square plastic construction materials.

18

Developing Numeracy
Measures, Shape and Space
Year 7
© A & C BLACK

Cube views

C

1. This is an ordinary 1 to 6 dice, where the numbers on opposite faces have a total of 7. A small piece of putty has been placed on one vertex of the dice.

(a) The dice is rotated without lifting it off the paper. Write the correct numbers on each blank face.

The putty helps you to see how the dice rotates.

(b) The dice is lifted and placed onto its side face. It is then rotated without lifting it again. Write the correct numbers on each blank face.

2. Using cubes, make all the possible shapes that can be made by fitting four cubes together, face to face. Draw the shapes on this isometric paper.

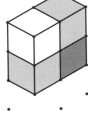

- Imagine that you are looking at a cube in your hand. Is it possible to hold the cube so that, at the same time, you can see exactly:

  1 face? _____ 2 faces? _____ 3 faces? _____ 4 faces? _____

- Explain your answers. Sketch the view for those that are possible.

 When you draw the shapes on isometric paper, you might find it helpful to colour the cubes to match the cubes you have fitted together. Make sure you colour the correct number of faces that you can see in each colour.

**Developing Numeracy
Measures, Shape and Space
Year 7
© A & C BLACK** 19

On reflection

1. Draw the reflection of triangle ABC in the mirror line (axis of reflection). Label the vertices of the image A' B' and C'.

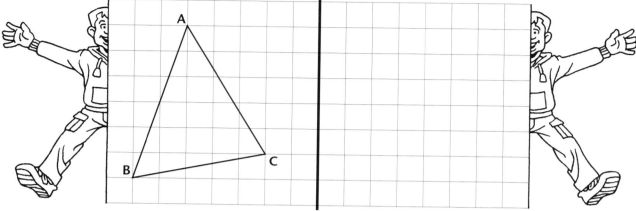

2. Draw straight lines to join: **(a)** A to A' **(b)** B to B' **(c)** C to C'

3. Tick the statements which are true.

(a) Each of the joining lines is **perpendicular** to the mirror line. ☐

(b) The distance from A to the mirror line is the same as from the mirror line to A'. ☐

(c) The distance from B to the mirror line is the same as from the mirror line to B'. ☐

(d) The distance from C to the mirror line is the same as from the mirror line to C'. ☐

(e) If you reflect A' in the mirror line, its image is A. ☐

B

1. Draw the reflection of the shape ABCD in the mirror line. First draw a line perpendicular to the mirror line from each vertex. Measure the distance from the vertex to the mirror line.

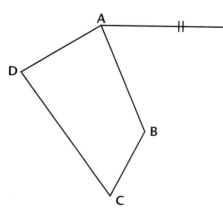

2. Draw a new shape and a mirror line on the back of this sheet. Use the same method to draw the reflection of the shape.

 The line joining a vertex and its image is **bisected** (cut in half) by the mirror line. The mirror line is always **perpendicular** (at right angles) to this line.

Developing Numeracy
Measures, Shape and Space
Year 7
© A & C BLACK

C

1. A triangle has one side that lies along an axis of symmetry. When the triangle is reflected, the shape and its image together make a quadrilateral.

(a) Draw the reflection of each triangle accurately. Name the quadrilateral.

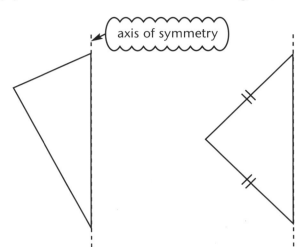

axis of symmetry

(b) Use a protractor to measure the angles in each quadrilateral. Mark them on the diagrams.

2. Draw the reflection of these letters in a vertical, horizontal and sloping mirror line.

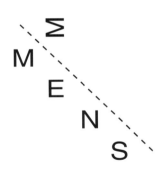

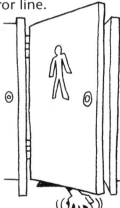

3. Which of the letters ⬚ ⬚ ⬚ oks the same when it is reflected in:

   (a) a vertical mirr ⬚   **(b)** a horizontal mirror line? _____

4. List all the capital l ⬚ ⬚abet that will look the same when they are reflected in:

   (a) a vertical mir ⬚ _____

   (b) a horizontal ⬚ _____

5. Which letter look ⬚ ⬚ it is reflected in a sloping mirror line? _____

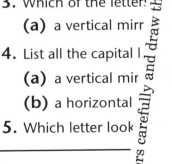

NOW TRY THIS!

 • Write words t ⬚ ⬚ ⬚ ne when they are reflected in:

   (a) a vertica ⬚   **(b)** a horizontal mirror line

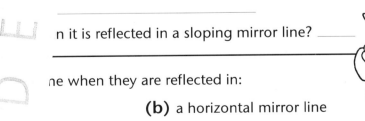

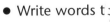

When letters ⬚ ⬚ ⬚ oping mirror line, you might find it easier to draw the ⬚ ⬚ n the paper so that the mirror line is vertical.

Developing Numeracy
Measures, Shape and Space
Year 7
© A & C BLACK

21

Symmetry sense

A Draw lines to show all the lines of symmetry in each pattern.

(a)

(b)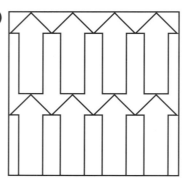

(c)

(d)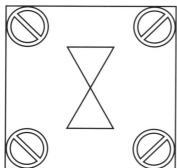

(e)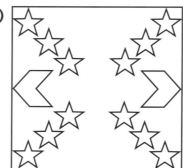

(f)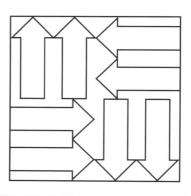

B **1.** Draw a pattern that has exactly:

(a) 2 lines of symmetry

(b) 4 lines of symmetry

2. How many lines of symmetry does each shape have?

(a)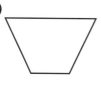

(b)

(c)

(d)

(e)

In part B, look carefully at the parallelogram. If you are not sure about its lines of symmetry, trace the shape and cut it out, then try folding it in different ways.

Developing Numeracy
Measures, Shape and Space
Year 7
© A & C BLACK

Symmetry sense

C 1. Play this game with a partner. You each need a counter and a different-coloured pen. You also need a dice.

☆ Player 1 rolls the dice and moves forward along the track to land on a shape.

☆ Together, players find the number of lines of symmetry of this shape. Player 1 scores that number of points and writes the number on the shape. This shape is no longer in the game.

☆ Take turns to move along the track, jumping over shapes which are no longer in play.

☆ The winner is the player with the most points when all the shapes are numbered.

START →

2. Five of the shapes above are **regular** shapes. Shade them. What is special about the number of lines of symmetry of regular shapes? _____

_____

NOW TRY THIS!
- There are eight nets for an open cube (an open cube is made from five squares). Draw them on squared paper.
- How many of these nets have reflection symmetry? _____

 If you are not sure about the number of lines of symmetry of a shape, trace the shape and cut it out, then try folding it in different ways.
Regular shapes are shapes with equal sides and equal angles.

Developing Numeracy
Measures, Shape and Space
Year 7
© A & C BLACK

23

Rotation, rotation

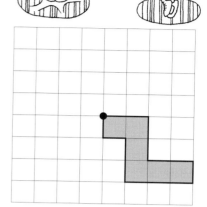

A Rotate each shape about the vertex marked with a dot.
Rotate the shape clockwise through 90°, 180° and 270°.
One has been done for you.

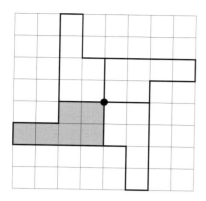
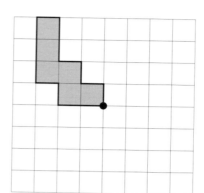
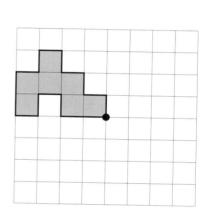

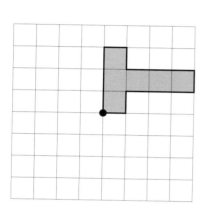
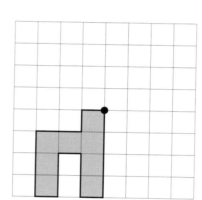

B Rotate this shape clockwise through 90° about the centres of rotation marked. One has been done for you.

Some of the images may lie over the original shape. !

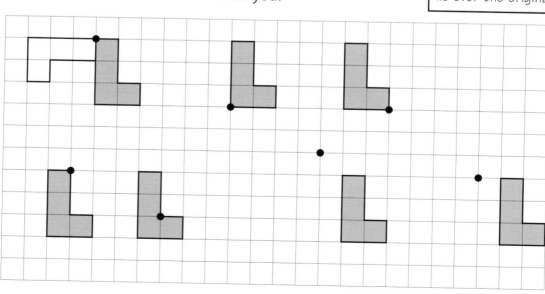

 To check your rotations, trace the shape and hold a pencil on the centre of rotation, then turn the tracing paper to check your image.

Developing Numeracy
Measures, Shape and Space
Year 7
© A & C BLACK

Rotation, rotation

C

1. Rotate each shape anticlockwise through the angle given, about the coordinate shown. Label the vertices of the image A', B' and C'.

(a)

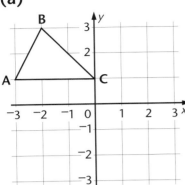

Through 180° about (0, 0)

(b)

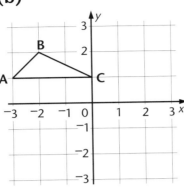

Through 90° about (0, 1)

(c)

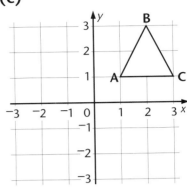

Through 270° about (1, 1)

2. Rotate these shapes anticlockwise. Draw the first rotation and label it. Then rotate your image by the second rotation.

(a)

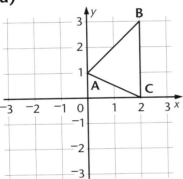

Through 180° about (0, 0), then through 180° about (0, 0)

(b)

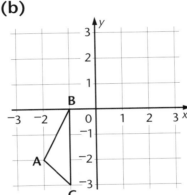

Through 90° about (⁻1, 1), then through 270° about (⁻1, 1)

(c)

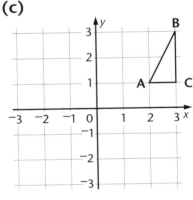

Through 270° about (1, 1), then through 90° about (1, 1)

(d) Write what you notice about rotations about the same point in the same direction with a total of 360°. _____

_____

NOW TRY THIS!

- On squared paper, draw a simple parallelogram and colour it yellow.

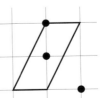

Example centres of rotation

- Rotate the shape clockwise through 90° using different centres of rotation.

  Choose centres of rotation that are:

  (a) at the vertices **(b)** inside the shape **(c)** outside the shape.

- Choose a colour for each of (a), (b) and (c). Colour the images in that colour.

 The first number in a pair of coordinates is the x-coordinate. It tells you how many across from zero to go. The second number is the y-coordinate. It tells you how many up or down from zero to go. To check your rotations, trace the shape and hold a pencil on the centre of rotation, then turn the tracing paper to check your image.

Keep on turning

A Find the | order of rotation symmetry | of each shape. This is the number of times the shape fits exactly into its outline when it is rotated through 360° about its centre.

(a)

5

(b)

(c)

(d)

(e)

(f)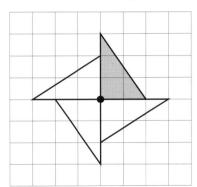

(g)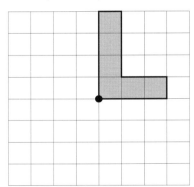

(h)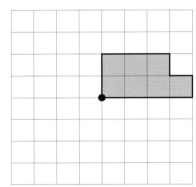

(i)

(j)

B

1. Keep rotating these non-symmetrical shapes about the dot through angles of 90°. This will make shapes with rotation symmetry of order 4. One has been done for you.

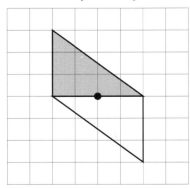

2. Rotate these shapes about the dot through angles of 180°. This will make shapes with rotation symmetry of order 2. One has been done for you.

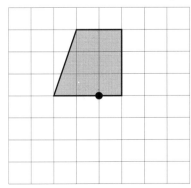
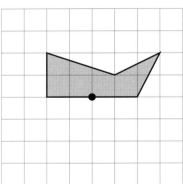

3. Through how many degrees should you repeatedly rotate a non-symmetrical shape to make a new shape with rotation symmetry of order 8?

To find the **order of rotation symmetry**, imagine turning the shape through 360° about its centre. As the shape turns, how many times does it fit exactly onto itself?

**Developing Numeracy
Measures, Shape and Space
Year 7**
© A & C BLACK

Keep on turning

C

1. This **isosceles triangle** has angles of 120°, 30° and 30°.

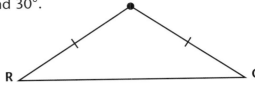

   (a) If the triangle is repeatedly rotated
   through 120° about point P,
   what shape will be made? _____

   (b) What will the **order of rotation symmetry** be? _____

   (c) Explain your answers. _____
   _____

2. Complete each pattern to make the order of rotation symmetry correct when the shape is rotated about its centre. Shade one or two more squares in each pattern.

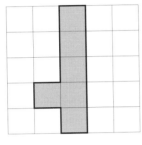   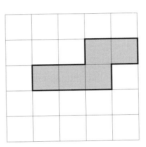   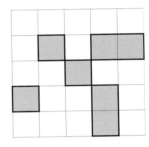

order 2   order 4   order 2   order 4

3. Complete each pattern to make the order of rotation symmetry correct when the shape is rotated about its centre. Shade three more squares in each pattern.

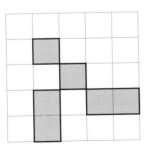   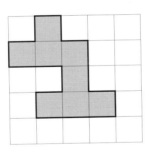   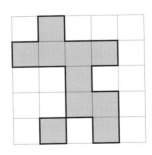   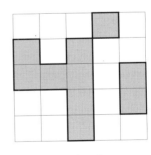

order 4   order 2   order 2   order 4

NOW TRY THIS!

- Combine two or three of these shapes to create shapes with rotation symmetry of order 2. Find at least six different ways. Draw the shapes on squared paper.

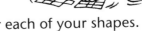

- Write the number of lines of reflection symmetry for each of your shapes.
- Make another puzzle like this for a partner to solve.

An **isosceles triangle** has two equal sides and two equal angles. To find the **order of rotation symmetry**, imagine turning the shape through 360° about its centre. As the shape turns, how many times does it fit exactly onto itself?

Be a translator

A 1. [Translate] each vertex according to the instructions given. Label the new points A', B', C', and so on. Join the points to make the image.

(a)

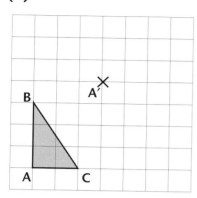

(b)

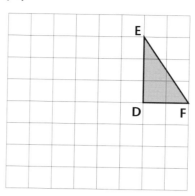

(c)

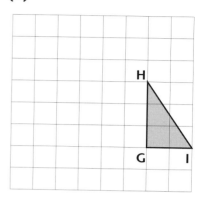

 Translate each vertex 3 squares to the right and 4 squares up.

 Translate each vertex 5 squares to the left and 1 square down.

Translate each vertex 4 squares to the left and 3 squares up.

2. The shaded shape has been translated and its image is shown. Write the [translation] that has taken place.

(a)

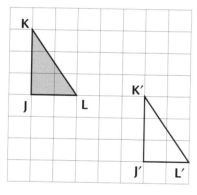

(b)

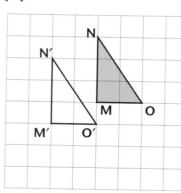

(c)

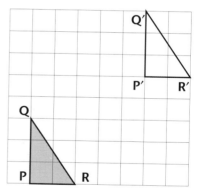

Translate each vertex _____

and _____ .

Translate each vertex _____

and _____ .

Translate each vertex _____

and _____ .

B Rewrite these translation instructions more simply.

(a) Translate 3 squares to the right and 5 squares up, and then 2 squares to the left.

_____

(b) Translate 6 squares to the left and 4 squares down, and then 7 squares up.

 To **translate** a shape, simply slide it in a particular direction for a particular distance. Do not turn it or reflect it in any way. A **translation** describes the direction and distance in which the shape has slid: for example, 5 units to the left, or 6 units to the right and 4 units up.

Developing Numeracy
Measures, Shape and Space
Year 7
© A & C BLACK

Be a translator

1. (a) Translate this triangle in different ways. Describe each **translation**.

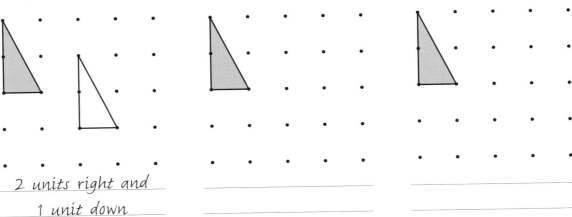

2 units right and
1 unit down

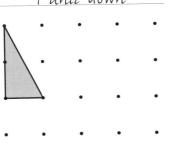

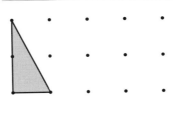

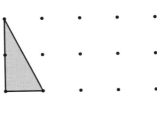

(b) How many different ways can you translate the shape on this grid of dots? Each vertex of the image must lie on one of the dots. _____

2. How many different ways could you translate each shape on these grids? Each vertex of the image must lie on one of the dots.

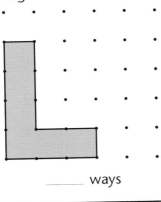

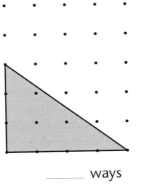

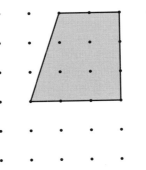

_____ ways   _____ ways   _____ ways

- Make a template on card of one of the shapes below.
- Make a [tessellating] pattern by translating the shape many times.

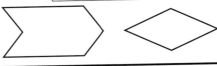 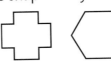 

 To **translate** a shape, slide it in a particular direction for a particular distance. A **translation** describes the direction and distance in which the shape has slid: for example, 5 units to the left, or 6 units to the right and 4 units up. To make a **tessellating** pattern, translate the same shape many times so that there are no spaces between the translated shapes.

What a transformation!

A Shape 1 is transformed to make shape 2, shape 2 is transformed to make shape 3, and so on. Write which type of transformation takes place each time.

> Choose from rotation, reflection or translation. Each rotation is 180° about the centre of the touching sides.

(a)

1 → 2 rotation, 2 → 3

(b)

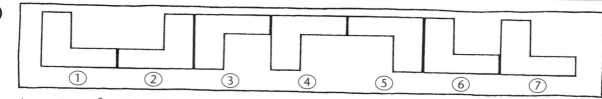

1 → 2 reflection, 2 → 3

(c)

1 → 2 translation, 2 → 3

B

1. Complete the missing words and images for these patterns.

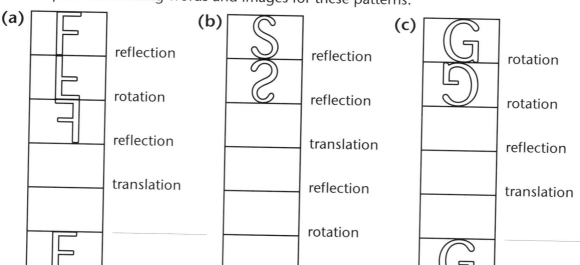

(a)
reflection

rotation

reflection

translation

(b)
reflection

reflection

translation

reflection

rotation

(c)
rotation

rotation

reflection

translation

2. Draw and label three more strips like this using other non-symmetrical letters.

 When you **transform** a shape, you rotate, reflect or translate it. Remember, when a shape is translated, it slides in a particular direction for a particular distance. Each rotation on this page is through 180°. In part A, each reflection is in a vertical mirror line. In part B, each reflection is in a horizontal mirror line.

Developing Numeracy
Measures, Shape and Space
Year 7
© A & C BLACK

What a transformation!

C

You need five different-coloured pencils.

1. (a) Colour the five squares of the centre shape **P**, making each square a different colour. Reflect shape **P** in the lines AB, BC, CD and DA.

(b) Now colour shape **Q** in exactly the same way as shape **P**. Reflect shape **Q** in the lines EF, FG, GH and HE.

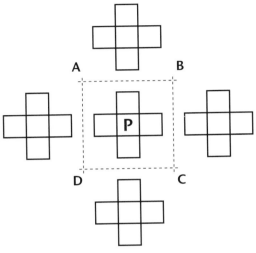

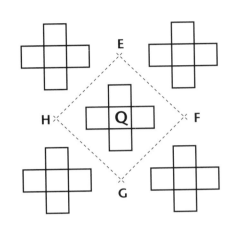

(c) What do you notice about the images of shapes P and Q? _____

2. (a) Colour the central shape **R** in the same colours as **P** and **Q**. Rotate **R** through 180° clockwise about each of the dots K, L, M and N in turn.

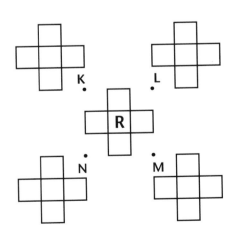

(b) What do you notice about the images of shape R?

_____

_____

(c) Are any of these rotations the same as any of the reflections in question 1?

_____

NOW TRY THIS!

- This triangle is reflected, rotated and **translated** on a 4 × 4 dotty grid. How many different ways can this be done? Each vertex of the image must lie on one of the dots.

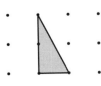

When you rotate the triangle in the 'Now try this!' challenge, you can use any dot inside, outside or on the edge of the triangle as the centre of rotation. You can turn the shape through any angle, as long as the vertices of the image lie on the dots. Remember, when a shape is **translated**, it slides in a particular direction for a particular distance.

**Developing Numeracy
Measures, Shape and Space
Year 7
© A & C BLACK**

31

Get coordinated!

A

1. Write the letter that lies at each of these coordinates.

(a) ($^-$4, 1) _B_

(b) (5, 7) _____

(c) (1, $^-$4) _____

(d) ($^-$5, 7) _____

(e) (7, 5) _____

(f) ($^-$7, 5) _____

(g) (4, 1) _____

(h) ($^-$1, 4) _____

(i) (0, $^-$1) _____

(j) ($^-$4, $^-$1) _____

Which two colours have you written?

2. Write the coordinates for the letters which spell: **RED** (_4_ , _$^-$1_) (___, ___) (___, ___)

PINK (___, ___) (___, ___) (___, ___) (___, ___)

CREAM (___, ___) (___, ___) (___, ___) (___, ___) (___, ___)

ORANGE (___, ___) (___, ___) (___, ___) (___, ___) (___, ___) (___, ___)

B

Describe the coordinates that lie in each quadrant of a grid.

(a) First quadrant x-coordinate _positive_

Example: (_3_ , _4_) y-coordinate _positive_

(b) Second quadrant x-coordinate _____

Example: (___, ___) y-coordinate _____

(c) Third quadrant x-coordinate _____

Example: (___, ___) y-coordinate _____

(d) Fourth quadrant x-coordinate _____

Example: (___, ___) y-coordinate _____

Second quadrant First quadrant

Third quadrant Fourth quadrant

In a pair of coordinates such as (3, 4) the first number is the x-coordinate. It tells you how many across from zero to go. The second number is the y-coordinate. It tells you how many up or down from zero to go. The phrase 'along the corridor and up or down the stairs' can help you remember the order. You could also think 'x is a cross, x is across'.

Developing Numeracy
Measures, Shape and Space
Year 7
© A & C BLACK

Get coordinated!

C

1. Plot these coordinates on the grid.

A (1, 7)

B (⁻5, 4)

C (1, 4)

D (2, 2)

E (⁻2, 1)

F (4, 1)

G (5, ⁻1)

H (⁻2, ⁻2)

I (⁻5, ⁻5)

J (1, ⁻5)

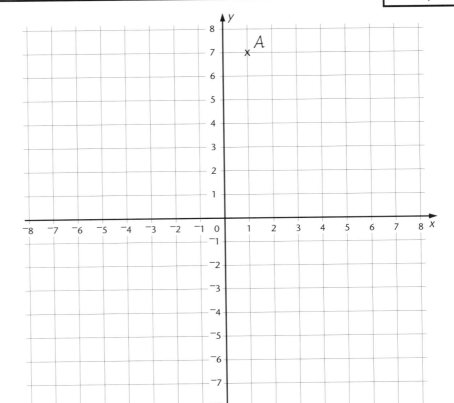

2. Look at the coordinates you have plotted. Which coordinates form the vertices of:

(a) a square? (__, __) (__, __) (__, __) (__, __)

(b) three different **isosceles triangles**? (__, __) (__, __) (__, __)

  (__, __) (__, __) (__, __)

  (__, __) (__, __) (__, __)

(c) a non-square rhombus? (__, __) (__, __) (__, __) (__, __)

(d) two non-square parallelograms? (__, __) (__, __) (__, __) (__, __)

  (__, __) (__, __) (__, __) (__, __)

(e) a non-square symmetrical **trapezium**? (__, __) (__, __) (__, __) (__, __)

(f) a trapezium with a right angle? (__, __) (__, __) (__, __) (__, __)

NOW TRY THIS!

- Follow the instructions to make a similar quiz. Give it to a partner to solve.

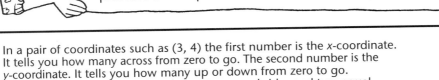

  ☆ Draw a coordinate grid and label the axes ⁻5 to 5.
  ☆ Draw the vertices of three different quadrilaterals overlapping on the grid. Find what other shapes can be made using these coordinates, such as isosceles triangles or other quadrilaterals.
  ☆ On a separate sheet, list the coordinates your partner needs to plot and the shapes to be found. Give this to your partner.

 In a pair of coordinates such as (3, 4) the first number is the x-coordinate. It tells you how many across from zero to go. The second number is the y-coordinate. It tells you how many up or down from zero to go. Remember, an **isosceles triangle** has two equal sides and two equal angles. A **trapezium** is a quadrilateral with one pair of parallel sides.

Quadrilateral quandary

A On each grid, draw a quadrilateral to match the description. The coordinates of the vertices must be whole numbers.

(a)

(b)

(c)

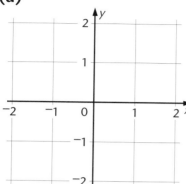
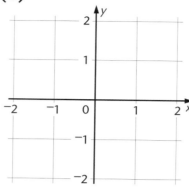
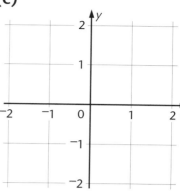

A square with no horizontal or vertical lines.

A **parallelogram** (not a rhombus) with no horizontal or vertical lines and no right angles.

A **trapezium** with a pair of vertical parallel lines.

(d)

(e)

(f)

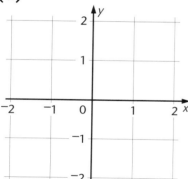
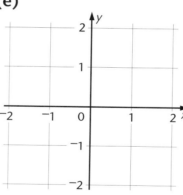
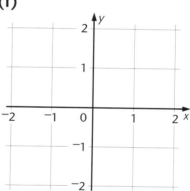

A kite with one right angle.

A **rhombus** with no horizontal or vertical lines (not a square).

A rectangle with no horizontal or vertical lines (not a square).

B 1. For each quadrilateral in part A, write the coordinates of the four vertices.

(a) (__, __) (__, __) **(b)** (__, __) (__, __) **(c)** (__, __) (__, __)
  (__, __) (__, __)   (__, __) (__, __)   (__, __) (__, __)

(d) (__, __) (__, __) **(e)** (__, __) (__, __) **(f)** (__, __) (__, __)
  (__, __) (__, __)   (__, __) (__, __)   (__, __) (__, __)

2. Which of your quadrilaterals have reflection symmetry? Sketch all the lines of symmetry.

3. Which of your quadrilaterals have **rotation symmetry**? Mark the centre of rotation.

 Remember, a **parallelogram** has two pairs of parallel sides. A **trapezium** has one pair of parallel sides. A **rhombus** is a parallelogram with sides of equal length. You may have drawn different shapes from those of your classmates, so your answers to part B may be different from theirs. A shape has **rotation symmetry** if you can rotate it to fit exactly onto itself.

Developing Numeracy
Measures, Shape and Space
Year 7
© A & C BLACK

Quadrilateral quandary

C

1. Plot the coordinates on the grids.

(a) (3, 1) (0, 2) (⁻3, 1)   **(b)** (0, 3) (1, ⁻1) (⁻2, 2)   **(c)** (1, 3) (1, ⁻2) (⁻2, ⁻3)

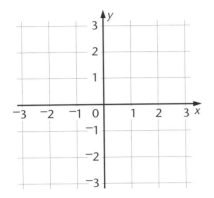
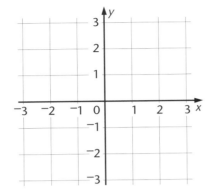
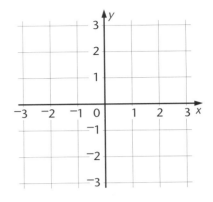

Imagine that the three points on each grid are three of the four vertices of a quadrilateral.

> The quadrilaterals must fit completely on the grid. There may be more than one answer.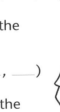

2. Write the coordinate that would be the fourth vertex if the quadrilateral was a **parallelogram**.

   (a) (___ , ___)   **(b)** (___ , ___)   **(c)** (___ , ___)

3. Write the coordinate that would be the fourth vertex if the quadrilateral was a **kite**.

   (a) (___ , ___)   **(b)** (___ , ___)   **(c)** (___ , ___)

4. Write the coordinate that would be the fourth vertex if the quadrilateral was a **trapezium**.

   (a) (___ , ___)   **(b)** (___ , ___)   **(c)** (___ , ___)

5. Is it possible to make a rectangle, using the three coordinates given and one other?

   (a) _____   **(b)** _____   **(c)** _____

   Explain your answers. _____

   _____

NOW TRY THIS!

- Make up three more puzzles like those in part C. Give them to a partner to solve. (Work out the answers too!)

 In a pair of coordinates such as (3, 4) the first number is the x-coordinate. It tells you how many across from zero to go. The second number is the y-coordinate. It tells you how many up or down from zero to go. Remember, a **parallelogram** is a quadrilateral with two pairs of parallel sides. A **trapezium** is a quadrilateral with one pair of parallel sides.

Measure up

A

1. Measure the length of each straw to the nearest millimetre.
Write the length in three different ways.

(a) _8 cm 9 mm,   8.9 cm,   89 mm_

(b) _____

(c) _____

(d) _____

(e) _____

(f) _____

(g) _____

(h) _____

(i) _____

2. (a) Draw vertical lines for each of these lengths.

7.4 cm   37 mm   6.2 cm   11 mm   5.8 cm   24 mm   69 mm   4.6 cm   7.3 cm

(b) Swap sheets with a partner. Check each other's measurements.

B

If these six lines were placed end-to-end and one extra line was added, the total length would be 715 mm.

How long is the extra line?
Give your answer in millimetres.

_____

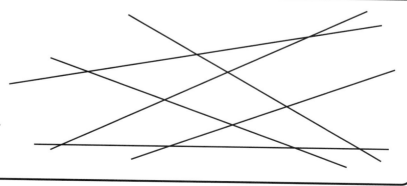

 To measure and draw lines accurately, make sure that you use a sharp pencil and look down on the ruler from directly above.

**Developing Numeracy
Measures, Shape and Space
Year 7**
© A & C BLACK

Use a ruler to measure and draw lines to the nearest mm

C

1. (a) Measure the sides of these shapes. Tick the six sides which measure 4.9 cm to the nearest millimetre.

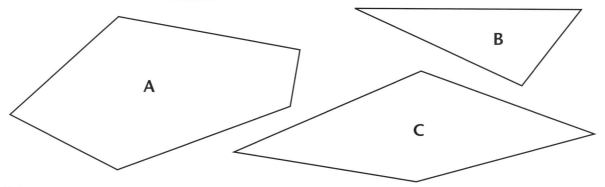

(b) Find the perimeter of each shape. Give your answer in millimetres.

Shape A _____   Shape B _____   Shape C _____

2. (a) Draw a pentagon with three of its sides 37 mm long to the nearest millimetre.

(b) Find the perimeter of your pentagon in millimetres.

_____

(c) Swap sheets with a partner. Check each other's measurements.

3. (a) Draw a square with 66 mm sides.

(b) Inside the square, draw a 56 mm line whose ends lie on two sides of the square. This line is one side of a new square with 56 mm sides. Draw the square.

(c) Now draw a 46 mm line that touches two sides of the new square. Draw a 46 mm square.

(d) In the same way, draw further squares inside with sides of 36 mm and 26 mm.

NOW TRY THIS!

•   Find the total length of the lines you have drawn to make your square pattern. Write your answer in three different ways.

_____   _____   _____

 Measure as carefully as you can. To measure and draw lines accurately, make sure that you use a sharp pencil and look down on the ruler from directly above.

**Developing Numeracy
Measures, Shape and Space
Year 7**
© A & C BLACK

37

Use a protractor to measure and draw angles to the nearest degree

At all angles

A Ann was asked to measure these angles to the nearest degree.
Use a protractor to check her work and correct her mistakes.

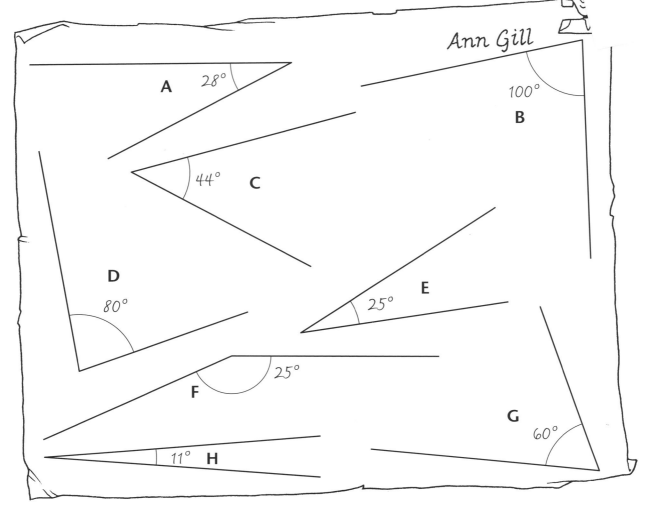

Ann Gill

A 28°

100°
B

44° C

D
80°

25° E

25°
F

G
60°

11° H

B **1.** For each pair of lines on Ann's work, draw a line joining the two end-points. This will give you eight triangles. Measure the other two angles in each triangle. Complete the table.

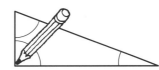

Triangle	Correct first angle	Second angle	Third angle	Sum of angles
A				
B				
C				
D				
E				
F				
G				
H				

2. What do you notice about the sum of the angles in a triangle? _____

When you use a protractor, start at zero and count around the protractor from one angle line to the other. This can help you to avoid using the wrong set of numbers on the protractor. Also think about whether the angle is acute or obtuse to check that your measurement is correct.

Developing Numeracy
Measures, Shape and Space
Year 7
© A & C BLACK

At all angles

1. Each shape below contains at least one | reflex angle |.

(a) Use a suitable method to measure each reflex angle. One has been done for you.

(b) Measure all the non-reflex angles.

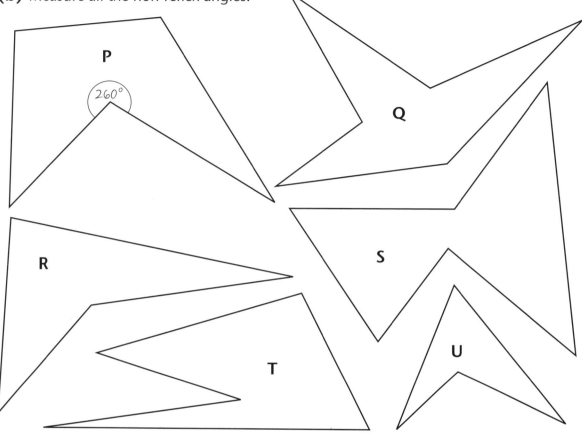

2. Work with a partner.

☆ Secretly choose a shape description from below.
☆ On a separate piece of paper, draw the shape accurately.
☆ Swap papers and identify your partner's shape description.

A quadrilateral with a reflex angle of 217°	A pentagon with a reflex angle of 264°	A hexagon with a reflex angle of 299°
A quadrilateral with a reflex angle of 227°	A pentagon with a reflex angle of 254°	A hexagon with a reflex angle of 301°
A quadrilateral with a reflex angle of 223°	A pentagon with a reflex angle of 256°	A hexagon with a reflex angle of 291°

NOW TRY THIS!

- Draw an **irregular** hexagon with at least one reflex angle.
- Measure all the interior angles and find the sum of the angles.
- Measure the lengths of the sides and find the perimeter.

A **reflex angle** is an angle between 180° and 360°. One method of measuring reflex angles is to use a protractor to measure the other angle in the full turn, then subtract this from 360° to give you the reflex angle.
Irregular shapes have unequal sides or angles.

Triangle tricks

A **(a)** In this diagram measure:

side AC = _____

angle A = _____

side AB = _____

(b) In this diagram measure:

angle D = _____

side DF = _____

angle F = _____

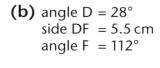

B **1.** Construct and label a triangle to match each description. One has been done for you.

(a) side AC = 7 cm
angle A = 32°
side AB = 4.5 cm

(b) angle D = 28°
side DF = 5.5 cm
angle F = 112°

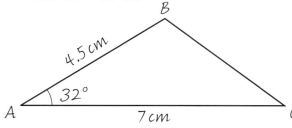

(c) side AC = 5.2 cm
angle A = 41°
side AB = 3.9 cm

(d) angle D = 17°
side DF = 6.8 cm
angle F = 86°

(e) side AC = 4.2 cm
angle A = 23°
side AB = 4.3 cm

(f) angle D = 134°
side DF = 3.7 cm
angle F = 13°

2. Measure and label the remaining sides and angles of your triangles. Check that the interior angles of each triangle have a sum of 180°.

3. Swap sheets with a partner. Check that each other's triangles are correct.

Measure as carefully as you can. You will need a ruler and a protractor.
To measure and draw lines accurately, make sure that you use a sharp
pencil and look down on the ruler or protractor from directly above.

Developing Numeracy
Measures, Shape and Space
Year 7
© A & C BLACK

C Solve these snail problems with a partner.
Work on an A3 piece of paper.

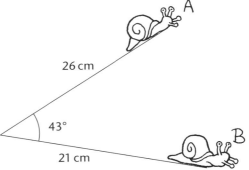

1. Two snails start at the same point. They crawl in
   different directions, each leaving a straight-line
   trail behind them. Snail A travels for 26 cm and
   snail B for 21 cm. Then they both stop.
   The angle between the trails is 43°.

   (a) Draw the trails on your paper.

   (b) How far away from each other are the two snails when they stop? _____

   (c) Snail A turns clockwise to face snail B. Through what angle does it turn? _____

   (d) Snail B turns anticlockwise to face snail A. Through what angle does it turn? _____

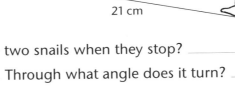

2. Snail C and snail D start exactly 26 cm apart,
   facing each other. Snail C turns anticlockwise
   through 37° and starts crawling in a straight
   line. Snail D turns clockwise through 42°
   and starts crawling in a straight line.

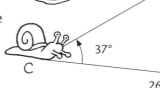

   (a) Draw the trails on your paper.

   (b) How far does snail C travel before it meets the path of snail D? _____

   (c) How far does snail D travel before it meets the path of snail C? _____

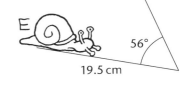

3. Snail E travels for 19.5 cm leaving a straight-line trail.
   It then turns anticlockwise and travels in a straight line for
   a further 22.5 cm. The angle between the two trails is 56°.

   (a) Draw the trails on your paper.

   (b) Snail E turns and crawls back to its starting point in a straight line.

   How far does snail E have to travel to reach its starting point? _____

   (c) Give all the angles of the triangle you have drawn. _____

NOW TRY THIS!

A snail leaves a trail that is the shape of a **rhombus**.
One of the angles of the rhombus is 84°. One side measures 19.2 cm.
• Construct the rhombus. Label each side and angle correctly.

Measure as carefully as you can. You will need a ruler and a protractor.
To measure and draw lines accurately, make sure that you use a sharp
pencil and look down on the ruler or protractor from directly above.
Remember, a **rhombus** has two pairs of parallel sides. All four sides are
of equal length.

Net constructions

1. Look at the dimensions of this cuboid. Measure the nets below. Tick the nets that match the cuboid.

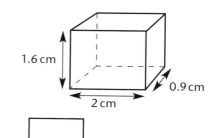

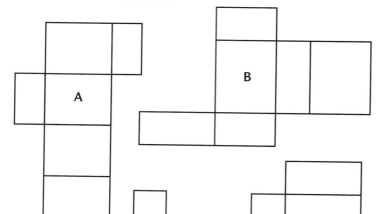

A

B

C

E

F

D

2. On a separate piece of paper or thin card, draw an accurate net for this cuboid.

Fold the net and make the cuboid to check.

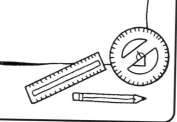

1.8 cm

1 cm

4 cm

B

1. This regular tetrahedron has edges that are 3 cm long. Each of its four faces is an **equilateral triangle**.

There are two possible nets of the tetrahedron. Use a protractor to construct both these nets below.

2. Swap sheets with a partner. Check each other's nets by measuring each side with a ruler and each angle with a protractor.

You will need a ruler and a protractor. To construct nets accurately, make sure that you use a sharp pencil and look down on the ruler or protractor from directly above. A **regular tetrahedron** has four identical faces. Each face is an **equilateral triangle**, which has three equal sides and three equal angles of 60°.

42

Developing Numeracy
Measures, Shape and Space
Year 7
© A & C BLACK

Net constructions

C This square-based pyramid has one square face and four faces that are **equilateral triangles**.

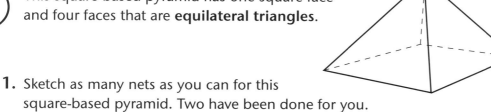

1. Sketch as many nets as you can for this square-based pyramid. Two have been done for you.

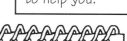

Use real shapes to help you.

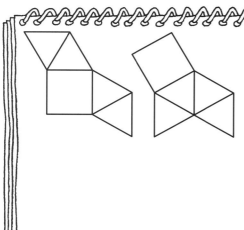

2. Ch___ ___ne of the nets above. Construct a net for a square-based pyramid that has ___ ___m long.

NOW TRY THIS!

- On thin card, construct a net of a triangular prism with these measurements.

- Before cutting out the net, work clockwise around the outline, adding a tab on every other edge.

- Make the triangular prism by folding the net and gluing the tabs.

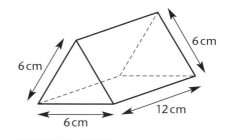

6 cm, 6 cm, 6 cm, 12 cm

You will need a ruler and a protractor. To construct nets accurately, make sure that you use a sharp pencil and look down on the ruler or protractor from directly above. Remember, an **equilateral triangle** has three equal sides and three equal angles of 60°.

Short measures

A Read these newspaper reports. Fill in the abbreviation for each unit.

(a) An American woman has toenails 152 millimetres long (152 _mm_) – that's 15.2 centimetres (15.2 _____).

(b) The planet Venus has a surface temperature of 480 degrees Celsius (480 _____).

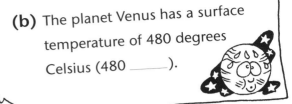

(c) The largest can of drink ever made was 4.5 metres high (4.5 _____). It weighed 300 kilograms (300 _____) and held nearly 3100 litres of drink (3100 _____).

(d) In 1999, Mongolia was the most sparsely populated country with approximately two people to every one square kilometre (1 _____).

In contrast, the island of Ap Lei Chau (Hong Kong) has about 60 000 people to every one square kilometre (1 _____).

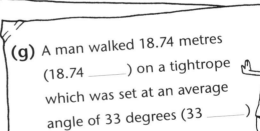

(e) The fastest time for cycling 100 metres (100 _____) on a unicycle from a standing start is 12.11 seconds (12.11 _____).

(g) A man walked 18.74 metres (18.74 _____) on a tightrope which was set at an average angle of 33 degrees (33 _____) from the horizontal.

(f) In 1997, a man stood on one foot for 76 hours and 40 minutes (76 _____ 40 _____).

B **1.** Convert these measurements to the units shown.

(a) 1 m = _____ cm   **(b)** 1 cm = _____ mm   **(c)** 1 m = _____ mm

(d) 1 km = _____ m   **(e)** 1 km = _____ cm   **(f)** 1 kg = _____ g

(g) 1 l = _____ ml   **(h)** 1 l = _____ cl   **(i)** 1 cl = _____ ml

(j) 1 min = _____ s   **(k)** 1 h = _____ min   **(l)** 1 h = _____ s

2. Which of the units above are measurements of:

(a) time _s,_ _____   **(b)** capacity _____

(c) length _____   **(d)** mass _____

The prefix *kilo-* means 1000: for example, a kilogram is 1000 grams, a kilometre is 1000 metres. The prefix *centi-* means 'one hundredth of', as in centimetre and centilitre. *Milli-* means 'one thousandth of'.

**Developing Numeracy
Measures, Shape and Space
Year 7**
© A & C BLACK

Short measures

C Play this estimating game with a partner or group.

☆ Your teacher will show you an item and ask you to estimate the length, mass or capacity of it using a particular unit.

☆ For each item, state two values that you think the real measurement might lie between. Find the range (the difference between your two values). The smaller your range, the more points you could score.

☆ Your teacher will give you the real measurement for the item. Write this down.

☆ Score 1 point if the value lies in your range, plus a further 3 points if you have the smallest range of everyone playing the game.

Item	Unit	Lowest value	Highest value	Range	Actual measurement	Score
Example mass of mobile phone	g	80 g	120 g	120 – 80 = 40	95 g	1 (+ 3 if no one else has a range smaller than 40)

NOW TRY THIS!

● Write a list of all the commonly used units of time. List them in order, from a second up to a millennium.

Mill-enn-i-um!

Remember that you can use decimals in your estimates (for example, 3.2 m or 15.8 cm).

**Developing Numeracy
Measures, Shape and Space
Year 7**
© A & C BLACK

Quick conversions

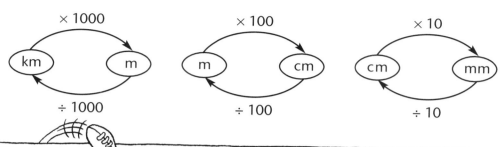

A

Use the diagrams to help you convert these lengths.

$\times 1000$ — km → m — $\div 1000$

$\times 100$ — m → cm — $\div 100$

$\times 10$ — cm → mm — $\div 10$

(a) 48 cm = __0.48__ m

(b) 137 cm = _____ m

(c) 54 mm = _____ cm

(d) 125 mm = _____ cm

(e) 1400 m = _____ km

(f) 1760 m = _____ km

(g) 5362 m = _____ km

(h) 467 m = _____ km

(i) 0.62 m = _____ cm

(j) 1.3 m = _____ cm

(k) 3.9 cm = _____ mm

(l) 13.2 cm = _____ mm

(m) 1.5 km = _____ m

(n) 1.53 km = _____ m

(o) 3.312 km = _____ m

(p) 0.47 km = _____ m

B

Use the diagrams to help you convert these measurements of mass and capacity.

$\times 1000$ — kg → g — $\div 1000$

$\times 1000$ — l → ml — $\div 1000$

$\times 100$ — l → cl — $\div 100$

$\times 10$ — cl → ml — $\div 10$

(a) 1200 g = __1.2__ kg

(b) 1640 g = _____ kg

(c) 4362 g = _____ kg

(d) 866 g = _____ kg

(e) 3.5 kg = _____ g

(f) 5.33 kg = _____ g

(g) 1.584 kg = _____ g

(h) 0.567 kg = _____ g

(i) 1647 ml = _____ l

(j) 530 cl = _____ l

(k) 5.8 cl = _____ ml

(l) 0.9 cl = _____ ml

(m) 16.67 l = _____ ml

(n) 6.732 l = _____ cl

When you multiply by 10, 100 or 1000, the digits of the number move across the columns to the left. When you divide by 10, 100 or 1000, the digits of the number move across the columns to the right.

Developing Numeracy
Measures, Shape and Space
Year 7
© A & C BLACK

C This table shows how the units of length are related.
Write pairs of equivalent measurements using the numbers in the table.

Look carefully at how the table works.

1000	100	10	1	0.1	0.01	0.001
km	–	–	m	–	cm	mm
9	0	0	0			
			6	9	5	
					4	2
		1	2	4	0	
				3	3	9

9 km = 9000 m

6.95 m = 695 cm

4.2 cm = 42 mm

12.4 m = 1240 cm

33.9 cm = 339 mm

	1000	100	10	1	0.1	0.01	0.001
(a)	6	3	4	0			
(b)				2	4	5	
(c)						3	8
(d)			2	7	5	0	
(e)					2	5	4
(f)	2	4	8	2			
(g)			7	5	8	0	
(h)					4	2	9
(i)				5	8	0	0

NOW TRY THIS!

- Use these cards to make at least 15 pairs of equal measurements. You do not have to use all the cards each time.

| km | m |
| cm | mm |

| 5 | 5 | 2 | 2 | 0 | 0 | 0 | 0 | . | . | = |

Example: 5.2 km = 5200 m

To convert between litres, centilitres and millilitres, you can draw a simpler version of the table above to use in the same way.

Master your measures

A

1. Tick the best estimate for each question.
   Which contestant wins the quiz?

		HUGO FURST	SADIE HANSA	JUSTIN TIME
(a)	Estimate the length of a football pitch.	13 m	100 m ✓	1 km
(b)	Estimate the mass of a 10p coin.	1 g	10 g	50 g
(c)	Estimate the area of the cover of an exercise book.	500 cm²	1 m²	50 cm²
(d)	Estimate the diameter of a CD.	120 mm	50 cm	50 mm
(e)	Estimate the capacity of a bath.	42 l	9999 ml	350 l
(f)	Estimate the distance from London to Paris.	35 km	400 km	2800 km
(g)	Estimate the mass of a box of tissues.	30 g	200 g	0.7 kg
(h)	Estimate the capacity of a teapot.	11 ml	$\frac{3}{4}$ l	3.5 l

2. Discuss your answers with a partner. Explain your reasoning.

B

Read the scales. Write the letters in order, from the heaviest item to the lightest.

You could convert them all to the same unit. !

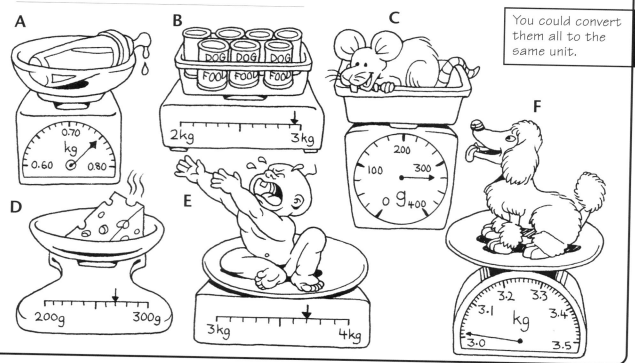

To read the scales in part B, find out what each small interval is worth by counting up the number of intervals between two given values and then dividing.

Developing Numeracy
Measures, Shape and Space
Year 7
© A & C BLACK

Master your measures

C

1. Read each scale. Record the reading and unit.

(a)

3.2 m　　　　　　　　　4.2 m

[*m*]

(b)

12 kg　　　　　　　　　22 kg

[　　　]

(c) 200 ml
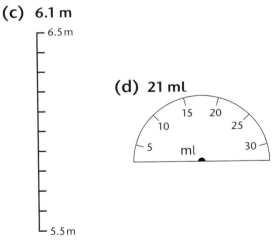
[　　　]

(d)

[　　　]

100 ml

(e) 1.7 l
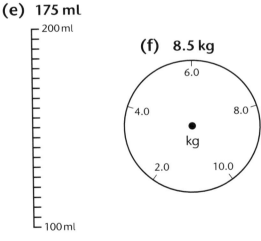

[　　　]

(f)

[　　　]

0.7 l

(g)
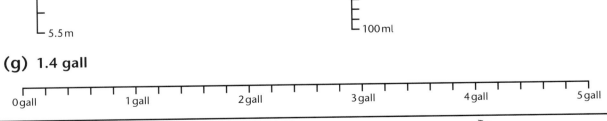
0 kg　　　　　　　　　　　　　　　　　　　　　　2.5 kg

[　　　]

2. Draw arrows on the scales to show these readings.

(a) 38.5 cm

30 cm　　　　　　　　　40 cm

(b) 14.5 m

10 m　　　　　　　　　20 m

(c) 6.1 m
6.5 m

(d) 21 ml

(e) 175 ml
200 ml

(f) 8.5 kg

5.5 m

100 ml

(g) 1.4 gall

0 gall　　　1 gall　　　2 gall　　　3 gall　　　4 gall　　　5 gall

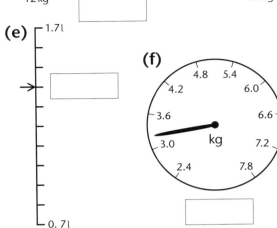

NOW TRY THIS!

- Suggest an item that each scale could be measuring.

To read the scales, find out what each small interval is worth by counting up the number of intervals between two given values and then dividing. In question 2, 'gall' is the abbreviation for gallons.

Got a problem?

A

1. Solve these measurement problems. Find each answer in the code below and colour its corresponding letter.

Workings

(a) Four suitcases weigh an average of 19.7 kg. What is the total mass of these cases?

(b) A teacup can hold 200 ml of tea and still have room for milk. A teapot holds 1.2 l of tea. How many cups can be poured from the teapot?

(c) A cake recipe requires 275 g of margarine. How many cakes can be made from a 1.1 kg tub of margarine?

(d) In a sweet factory, a 1.2 metre stick of rock is cut into chunks which are 24 mm long. How many chunks can be made from this stick?

(e) If 454 mm of rope is cut from a length 4.5 m long, how much rope is left?

(f) A sofa is 168 cm long. A shop displays this sofa and a matching chair next to each other, without a gap between. The two items fit exactly along the side of a 2.5 m wall. How wide is the chair?

(g) A CD weighs 20 g and its case weighs 35 g. How many CDs in their cases are there in a bundle of CDs weighing 0.66 kg?

(h) Seven houses are joined as a terrace. Each house is 3.92 m wide. What is the width of the terrace?

(i) Dried apricots cost £5.60 per kilogram. If each apricot costs 7p, what is the average mass of an apricot?

12.5 g	788 g	404.6 cm	125 g	82 cm	4	6	50	5	27.44 m	78.8 kg	12
E	C	U	Y	O	N	A	T	P	Q	I	S

2. Make a mathematical word using the coloured letters. _____

B

How many 24 mm chunks can be cut from a stick of rock measuring:

(a) 144 cm? **(b)** 1.92 m? **(c)** 0.84 m? **(d)** 936 mm? **(e)** 40.8 cm?

Watch out for the different units in some questions. Always convert the measurements to the same unit before calculating.

Developing Numeracy
Measures, Shape and Space
Year 7
© A & C BLACK

C

1. Strips of paper are stapled together in one long strand to use as a decoration.
   Each strip of paper is 20 cm long. The strips overlap each other by 2 cm.

   20 cm

   2 cm

   How long is a strand made from:

   (a) 2 strips of paper? _____   **(b)** 3 strips of paper? _____

   (c) 4 strips of paper? _____   **(d)** 5 strips of paper? _____

   How many strips of paper are used to make a strand measuring:

   (e) 110 cm? _____   **(f)** 146 cm? _____

   (g) 2 m? _____   **(h)** 2.54 m? _____

2. Another decoration is made using triangles of sticky paper,
   which are rotated and stuck onto a circle of card.

   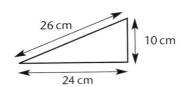

   26 cm   10 cm   24 cm

   For this octagonal pattern, find:

   (a) the area _____   **(b)** the perimeter _____

3. This decoration is made in a similar way, using **isosceles triangles**.

   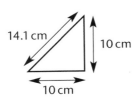

   14.1 cm   10 cm   10 cm

   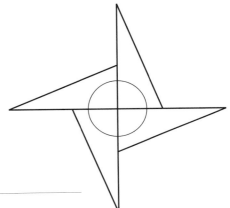

   For this 16-sided pattern, find:

   (a) the area _____   **(b)** the perimeter _____

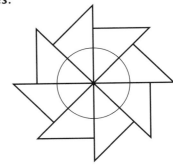

4 cm   45°   135°   7 cm   7 cm   135°   45°   4 cm

NOW TRY THIS!

- Construct an accurate template of this shape on card.
- Use the template to draw and cut out several shapes. Make different patterns by joining sides of the shapes together.
- Write the area and perimeter of each pattern.

Remember, an **isosceles triangle** has two equal sides and two equal angles. The formula for finding the area of a right-angled triangle is $\frac{1}{2} \times$ base $\times$ height. For the 'Now try this!' challenge, you will need a ruler, protractor, sharp pencil and scissors. To find the area of a parallelogram, multiply the base by the perpendicular height.

Developing Numeracy
Measures, Shape and Space
Year 7
© A & C BLACK
51

Angle antics

A A washing machine has a circular dial that moves to show the washing cycle. An arrow moves clockwise, starting at the top. Write whether the shaded angle is **acute**, **right**, **obtuse**, **straight** or **reflex**. **Estimate** the size of this angle.

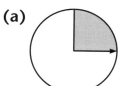

(a) 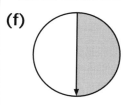   **(b)**    **(c)** 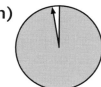   **(d)**   **(e)**

right
90°

(f)   **(g)** 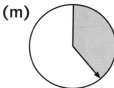   **(h)** 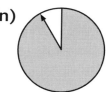   **(i)** 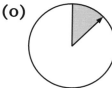   **(j)**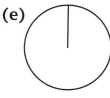

(k) 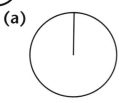   **(l)** 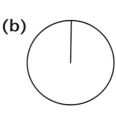   **(m)** 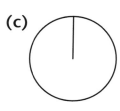   **(n)** 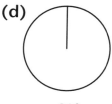   **(o)**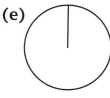

B **Estimate** where the arrow should be for each angle. Draw it on the dial.

(a) 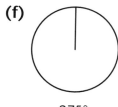   **(b)** 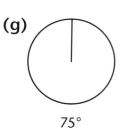   **(c)** 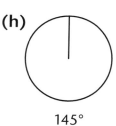   **(d)** 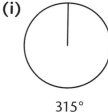   **(e)**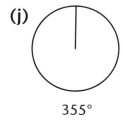

120°   290°   190°   20°   240°

(f)   **(g)**   **(h)**   **(i)**   **(j)**

275°   75°   145°   315°   355°

 An **acute angle** is less than 90°, a **right angle** is 90°, an **obtuse angle** is between 90° and 180°, a **straight angle** is 180°, and a **reflex angle** is between 180° and 360°.

Developing Numeracy
Measures, Shape and Space
Year 7
© A & C BLACK

Angle antics

C

1. Join one dot to two others to form an angle. Mark the angle with an arc. Do this twice in each box. Write a description of each angle and **estimate** its size.

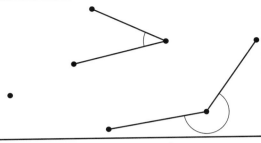

Acute angle about 40°
Reflex angle about 225°

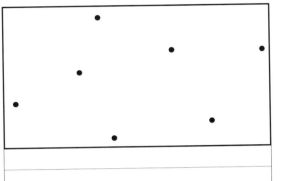

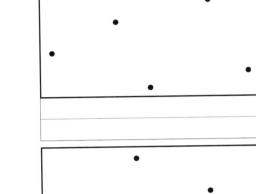

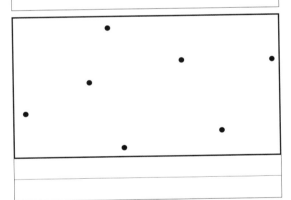

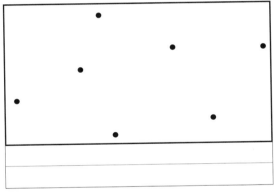

2. In the same way, draw angles to match each of these descriptions.

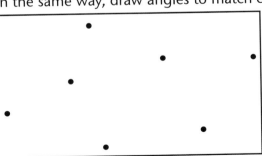

Reflex angle about 320°
Acute angle about 15°

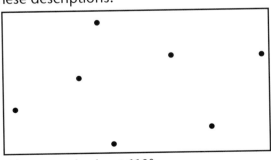

Obtuse angle about 110°
Right angle 90°

NOW TRY THIS!

- Measure each angle with a protractor and label it.
- Discuss with a partner how close your estimates were.

An **acute angle** is less than 90°, a **right angle** is 90°, an **obtuse angle** is between 90° and 180°, a **straight angle** is 180°, and a **reflex angle** is between 180° and 360°. In the 'Now try this!' challenge, extend the angle lines if you need to. To measure a reflex angle, you could measure the other angle in the full turn, then subtract this from 360°.

Developing Numeracy
Measures, Shape and Space
Year 7
© A & C BLACK

53

You'd better shape up!

A Find the area of each shape in square centimetres (cm²). Count the squares and half squares.

(a)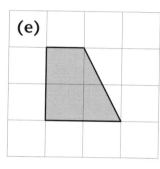

Area = _6 cm²_

(b)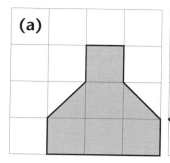

Area = _____

(c)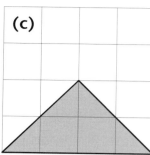

Area = _____

(d)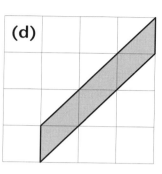

Area = _____

(e)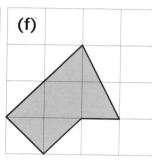

Area = _____

(f)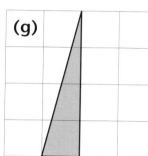

Area = _____

(g)

Area = _____

(h)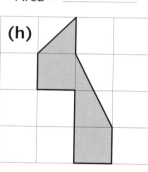

Area = _____

B **1.** Shade different shapes that have an area of $7\frac{1}{2}$ cm².

Try to include triangles.

2. Swap sheets with a partner. Check the areas of each other's shapes. Which of your shapes has the greatest number of sides?

 To find the area of a right-angled triangle, imagine a rectangle split in half diagonally to make two right-angled triangles. Find the area of the rectangle, then halve it to give the area of one triangle.

Developing Numeracy
Measures, Shape and Space
Year 7

54

You'd better shape up!

C

1. In each grid below, draw a *different* quadrilateral whose vertices touch the dots. Do not draw rectangles or squares. Rotations, translations and reflections of the same shape should not be included.

The area of a right-angled triangle is half the area of the rectangle.

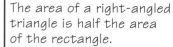

2. Find the area of each shape using one of the methods below.
   ☆ Split the shape into rectangles and right-angled triangles
   or
   ☆ Find the area of a larger rectangle and subtract the outer shapes.

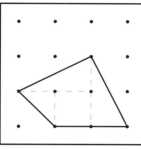

Area = $\frac{1}{2}$ + 1 + 1 + 1
= $3\frac{1}{2}$

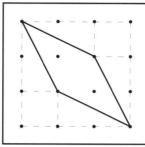

Area = 9 − 6 = 3

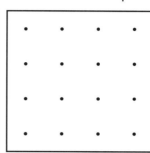

Area =

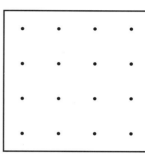

Area =

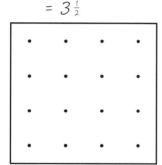

Area =

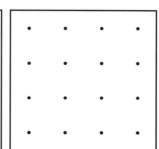

Area =

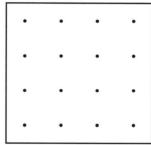

Area =

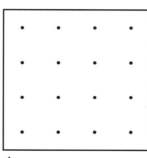

Area =

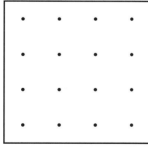

Area =

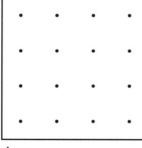

Area =

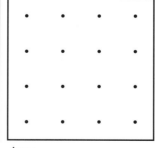

Area =

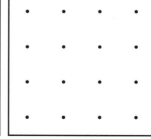

Area =

3. Compare your shapes with a partner's. Did you use the same method to find the area of each shape?

WALKIES!

NOW TRY THIS!

- Draw ten **isosceles triangles** on square dotty paper.
- Find the area of each triangle using one of the methods above.

 To find the area of a right-angled triangle, first multiply the base by the height to find the area of the rectangle, then halve it. Remember, an **isosceles triangle** has two equal sides and two equal angles.

Developing Numeracy Measures, Shape and Space Year 7
© A & C BLACK

55

Area realities

A Calculate mentally the perimeter and area of each photograph.

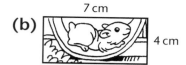 The rectangles are not drawn to scale.

(a)
8 cm
5 cm

Perimeter = __26 cm__

Area = __40 cm²__

(b)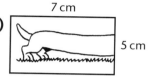
7 cm
4 cm

Perimeter = _____

Area = _____

(c)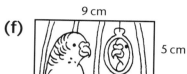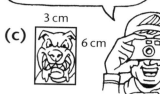
3 cm
6 cm

Perimeter = _____

Area = _____

(d)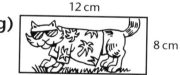
7 cm
5 cm

Perimeter = _____

Area = _____

(e)
10 cm
3 cm

Perimeter = _____

Area = _____

(f)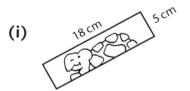
9 cm
5 cm

Perimeter = _____

Area = _____

(g)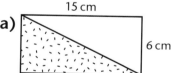
12 cm
8 cm

Perimeter = _____

Area = _____

(h)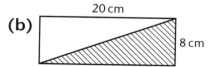
11 cm   11 cm

Perimeter = _____

Area = _____

(i)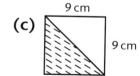
18 cm   5 cm

Perimeter = _____

Area = _____

B **1.** Find the area of each rectangle. Then find the area of each patterned triangle.

(a)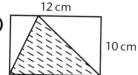
15 cm
6 cm

Rectangle = _____ cm²

Triangle = _____ cm²

(b)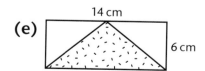
20 cm
8 cm

Rectangle = _____

Triangle = _____

(c)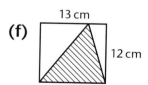
9 cm
9 cm

Rectangle = _____

Triangle = _____

(d)
12 cm
10 cm

Rectangle = _____

Triangle = _____

(e)
14 cm
6 cm

Rectangle = _____

Triangle = _____

(f)
13 cm
12 cm

Rectangle = _____

Triangle = _____

2. The formula for finding the area of a rectangle is $\boxed{A = b \times h}$, where b is the length of the base and h is the height. What is the formula for finding the area of a triangle? _____

 The formulae for finding the perimeter and area of a rectangle are:
Perimeter = 2(l + w) and **Area = l × w**, where *l* is length and *w* is width.
The formula for finding the area of a triangle is $\frac{1}{2}$ × base × perpendicular height.

Developing Numeracy
Measures, Shape and Space
Year 7
© A & C BLACK

Area realities

C

1. Find the area of each shape by splitting it into rectangles.

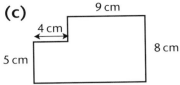
The shapes are not drawn to scale.

(a)
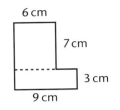
6 cm
7 cm
3 cm
9 cm

Area = _69 cm²_

(b)
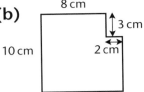
8 cm
3 cm
2 cm
10 cm

Area = _____

(c)
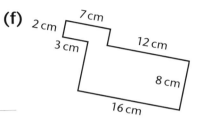
9 cm
4 cm
5 cm
8 cm

Area = _____

(d)
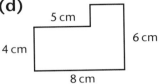
5 cm
4 cm
6 cm
8 cm

Area = _____

(e)
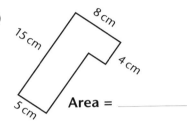
8 cm
15 cm
4 cm
5 cm

Area = _____

(f)
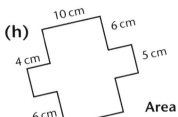
2 cm
7 cm
3 cm
12 cm
8 cm
16 cm

Area = _____

(g)
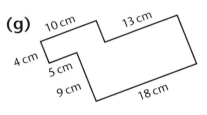
10 cm
13 cm
4 cm
5 cm
9 cm
18 cm

Area = _____

(h)
10 cm
6 cm
4 cm
5 cm
6 cm

Area = _____

2. Find the area of the shaded part of each shape. First find the area of the whole shape, then subtract the area of the unshaded part or parts.

(a)
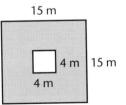
15 m
4 m
15 m
4 m

Area = _____

(b)
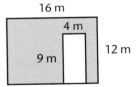
16 m
4 m
9 m
12 m

Area = _____

(c)
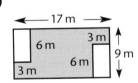
17 m
6 m
3 m
3 m
6 m
9 m

Area = _____

(d)
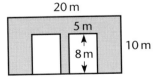
20 m
5 m
8 m
10 m

Area = _____

(e)
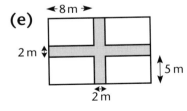
8 m
2 m
5 m
2 m

Area = _____

NOW TRY THIS!

● Draw five different shapes, each with an area of 48 cm².

Use subtraction or addition to find the lengths of sides that have not been given. You may find it helpful to write in the lengths of all the sides before calculating.

Deduce and solve
problems relating
to surface areas

On the surface

A

1. Imagine covering the surfaces of these cubes completely with 1 cm² stickers. How many stickers would you need for each cube?

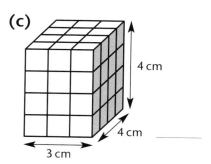

(a)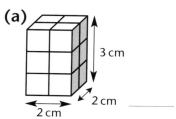

1 cm, 1 cm, 1 cm

6

(b) 2 cm, 2 cm, 2 cm

(c) 3 cm, 3 cm, 3 cm

(d) 4 cm, 4 cm, 4 cm

2. Imagine covering these cuboids in the same way. How many stickers would you need for each?

(a)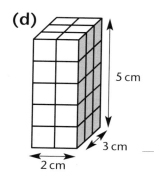

3 cm, 2 cm, 2 cm

(b)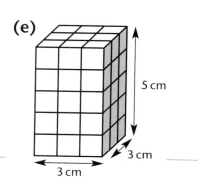

4 cm, 3 cm, 2 cm

(c)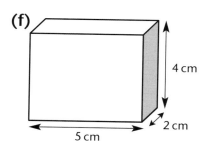

4 cm, 4 cm, 3 cm

(d) 5 cm, 2 cm, 3 cm

(e) 5 cm, 3 cm, 3 cm

(f) 4 cm, 5 cm, 2 cm

B

The formula for the surface area (*S*) of a cuboid can be written as
$S = 2bl + 2lh + 2hb$, where *b* is breadth, *l* is length and *h* is height.

Use this formula to check your answers to question 2 in part A.

(a) $S = 2(2 \times 2) + 2(2 \times 3) + 2(3 \times 2) = 8 + 12 + 12 =$

(b) _____

(c) _____

(d) _____

(e) _____

(f) _____

 The surface area of a 3-D shape is the amount of surface on all of its faces added together. To find the surface area, you can visualise each face and find the area, or you can use the formula $S = 2bl + 2lh + 2hb$, where *S* is surface area, *b* is breadth, *l* is length and *h* is height.

Developing Numeracy
Measures, Shape and Space
Year 7
© A & C BLACK

On the surface

C

1. (a) Construct all the different cuboids that can be made from 24 cubes. Sketch the cuboids and label the dimensions.

You need centimetre interlocking cubes.

4 cm
2 cm
3 cm

(b) Find the surface area (*S*) of each cuboid. You could use the formula
$S = 2bl + 2lh + 2hb$, where *b* is breadth, *l* is length and *h* is height.

2. Make these shapes using interlocking cubes. Find the surface area of each shape.

(a)

_____ *cm*²

(b)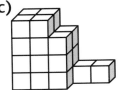

(c)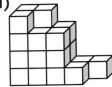

(d)

(e)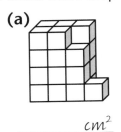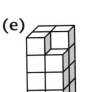

(f)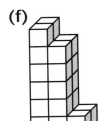

(g)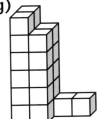

(h)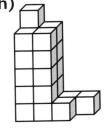

NOW TRY THIS!

• Find the surface area of each of these shapes.

(a)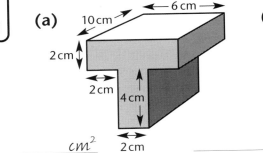

10 cm
6 cm
2 cm
2 cm
4 cm
2 cm

_____ *cm*²

(b)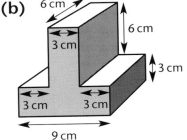

6 cm
6 cm
3 cm
3 cm
3 cm
3 cm
9 cm

(c)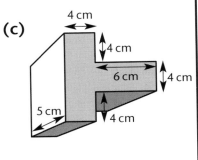

4 cm
4 cm
6 cm
4 cm
5 cm
4 cm

 The surface area of a 3-D shape is the amount of surface on all of its faces added together. To find the surface area, you can visualise each face and find the area, or you can use the formula **S = 2bl + 2lh + 2hb**, where *S* is surface area, *b* is breadth, *l* is length and *h* is height.

**Developing Numeracy
Measures, Shape and Space
Year 7**
© A & C BLACK **59**

Answers

p 8

A1 straight
intersect
intersection
segment
parallel
angle
polygon
plane
vertices

B The first, second and sixth triangles are labelled correctly.

p 9

C1 (a) True (b) False
(c) False (d) False
(e) True (f) True
(g) False (h) False
(i) True (j) False
(k) False (l) True
(m) True (n) True

C2 (a) Yes
(b) Yes

Now try this!
(a) No
(b) Yes

p 10

A1 Outer region – A I V X Y
Parallel only – M N W Z
Perpendicular only – L T J K
Intersection – E F H

B $a = c$ $b = d$ $a + b + c + d = 360°$
$a + b = 180°$ $b + c = 180°$
$c + d = 180°$ $a + d = 180°$
$180° - b = a$ **or** $180° - b = c$
$360° - c = a + b + d$

p 11

C (a) False (b) True
(c) True (d) True
(e) False (f) True
(g) True (h) True
(i) False (j) True
(k) False (l) True
(m) False (n) False
(o) True (p) True
(q) True (r) True
(s) True (t) True

p 12

A Statements equivalent to 90°, 180° or 360°: for example, $d + e + f + g = 360°$

B (a) $a = 45°$
$b = 45°$
(b) $c = 70°$
$d = 40°$
(c) $e = 320°$
$f = 70°$
$g = 70°$
(d) $h = 30°$
$i = 75°$
$j = 75°$
(e) $k = 65°$
$l = 65°$
$m = 50°$
(f) $n = 45°$
$o = 45°$
$p = 90°$

p 13

C (a) $a = 120°$
(b) $b = 135°$
$c = 45°$
$d = 135°$
(c) $e = 30°$
(d) $f = 50°$
(e) $g = 135°$
$h = 45°$
(f) $i = 30°$
(g) $j = 105°$
(h) $k = 60°$
(i) $l = 45°$

Now try this!
(a) 60° (b) 45°
(c) 36° (d) 30°

p 14

A1 (a) Yes
(b) Yes
(c) Isosceles triangle with 45° and 90° angles

A2 (a) No
(b) No
(c) Isosceles triangle

p 15

C1

(a)  (b)   (c)

(d)   (e) Example: (f)

(g) Example: (h) Example: (i) Example:

Now try this!
Example answers:

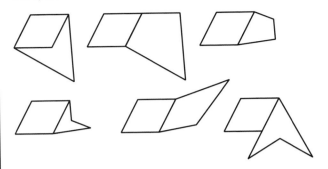

p 16

B1 (a) 60°, 60°, 60°
(b) 120°, 30°, 30°
(c) 90°, 30°, 60°
(d) 120°, 120°, 60°, 60°
(e) 120°, 60°, 120°, 60°
(f) 90°, 90°, 90°, 90°
(g) 120°, 90°, 60°, 90° **or** 60°, 30°, 240°, 30°
(h) 120°, 120°, 120°, 120°, 120°, 120°

B2 (a) 180°　　(b) 360°　　(c) 720°

p 17

Now try this!
Rectangle, scalene triangle, square

p 19

Now try this!
3 faces, 2 faces and 1 face are possible.

p 20

A3 All the statements are true.

p 21

C3 (a) M　　(b) E
C4 (a) A H I M O T U V W X Y
(b) B C D E H I K O X
C5 X

p 22

A (a) 4　　(b) 1　　(c) 2
(d) 1　　(e) 2　　(f) 0
B2 (a) 1　　(b) 2　　(c) 3
(d) 0　　(e) 4

p 23

Now try this!
3

p 26

A (a) 5　(b) 2　(c) 3　(d) 4　(e) 1
(f) 2　(g) 4　(h) 4　(i) 1　(j) 6

p 27

C1 (a) Equilateral triangle
(b) 3

C2

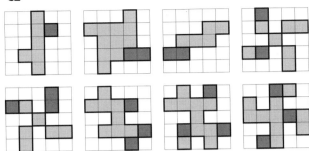

p 28

A2 (a) 5 squares to the right and 3 squares down
(b) 2 squares to the left and 1 square down
(c) 5 squares to the right and 5 squares up

B (a) 1 square to the right and 5 squares up
(b) 6 squares to the left and 3 squares up

p 29

C1 (b) 11

C2 5 ways, 5 ways, 8 ways

p 30

A (a) rotation, reflection, translation, rotation, reflection
(b) reflection, rotation, translation, reflection, rotation, translation
(c) translation, reflection, rotation, rotation, reflection, rotation, reflection

B1 (a) rotation
(c) reflection

p 31

Now try this!
There are 47 images; five of these are translations. The shape and its five translations can each be rotated through 90°, 180° and 270°. Each of these can be reflected, to make 24 reflections.

p 32

A1 BLACK
WHITE

A2 RED:　　(4, ⁻1) (⁻4, ⁻1) (⁻1, 0)
PINK:　　(⁻5, ⁻7) (⁻1, 4) (⁻7, ⁻5) (7, 5)
CREAM:　(⁻5, 7) (4, ⁻1) (⁻4, ⁻1) (1, ⁻4) (7, ⁻5)
ORANGE: (5, ⁻7) (4, ⁻1) (1, ⁻4) (⁻7, ⁻5) (⁻1, ⁻4) (⁻4, ⁻1)

B (a) positive
positive
(b) negative
positive
(c) negative
negative
(d) positive
negative

p 33

C2 Possible answers:
(a) (1, 7) (⁻5, 4) (⁻2, ⁻2) (4, 1)
(b) (⁻2, 1) (⁻5, ⁻5) (1, ⁻5)
(⁻2, 1) (4, 1) (1, 4)
(⁻2, 1) (4, 1) (1, ⁻5)
(c) (1, 7) (⁻2, 1) (1, ⁻5) (4, 1)
(d) (⁻5, ⁻5) (⁻2, 1) (4, 1) (1, ⁻5)
(⁻5, 4) (1, 4) (4, 1) (⁻2, 1)
(e) (⁻5, 4) (⁻2, 1) (⁻2, ⁻2) (⁻5, ⁻5)
(f) (1, 7) (⁻5, 4) (⁻5, ⁻5) (1, ⁻5)

p 35

C2 (a) (0, ⁻2)
(b) (⁻1, ⁻2) **or** (3, 0)
(c) (⁻2, 2)

C3 (a) Any of the following:
(0, ⁻1) (0, ⁻2) (0, ⁻3) (0, 3) (0, 0)
(b) (⁻3, 0)
(c) (⁻3, 0) **or** (2, 3)

C4 (a) (3, ⁻1) **or** (⁻3, ⁻1)
(b) (⁻3, ⁻3) **or** (3, 0)
(c) Any of the following:
(⁻2, ⁻1) (⁻2, ⁻2) (⁻2, 0) (⁻2, 1) (⁻2, 3)

C5 (a) No　　　(b) No　　　(c) No

p 36

A1 (a) 8 cm 9 mm, 8.9 cm, 89 mm
(b) 6 cm 4 mm, 6.4 cm, 64 mm
(c) 7 cm 6 mm, 7.6 cm, 76 mm
(d) 4 cm 1 mm, 4.1 cm, 41 mm
(e) 5 cm 1 mm, 5.1 cm, 51 mm
(f) 8 cm 2 mm, 8.2 cm, 82 mm
(g) 2 cm 3 mm, 2.3 cm, 23 mm
(h) 7 cm 4 mm, 7.4 cm, 74 mm
(i) 8 cm 7 mm, 8.7 cm, 87 mm

B 193 mm

p 37

C1 (b) A = 187 mm　B = 135 mm　C = 202 mm

Now try this!
920 mm, 92 cm, 0.92 m

p 38

A A　Correct
B　Incorrect (80°)
C　Correct
D　Correct
E　Correct
F　Incorrect (155°)
G　Incorrect (65°)
H　Incorrect (9°)

B1 A　28°, 50°, 102°
B　80°, 50°, 50°
C　44°, 59°, 77°
D　80°, 58°, 42°
E　25°, 90°, 65°
F　155°, 12.5°, 12.5°
G　65°, 47°, 68°
H　9°, 87°, 84°

B2 The sum of the angles in a triangle is always 180°.

p 39

C1 Angles given in clockwise order, starting at top left:
P　97°, 115°, 28°, 260°, 40°
Q　26°, 240°, 24°, 140°, 30°, 260°
R　82°, 21°, 221°, 36°
S　57°, 235°, 41°, 43°, 276°, 68°
T　35°, 99°, 64°, 9°, 333°
U　59°, 25°, 251°, 25°

p 40

A (a) side AC = 6 cm
angle A = 32°
side AB = 6 cm

(b) angle D = 25°
side DF = 6 cm
angle F = 110°

p 41

All answers are approximate.
C1 (b) 18 cm
(c) 127°
(d) 97°

C2 (b) 18 cm
(c) 16 cm

C3 (b) 19.5 cm
(c) 56°, 56°, 68°

Now try this!
All sides are 19.2 cm.
Angles are 84°, 96°, 84°, 96°.

p 42

A1 B, E and F

p 44

A (a) mm, cm　　(b) °C
(c) m, kg, l　　(d) km², km²
(e) m, s
(f) h, min
(g) m, °

B1 (a) 100　　(b) 10　　　(c) 1000
(d) 1000　　(e) 100 000　(f) 1000
(g) 1000　　(h) 100　　　(i) 10
(j) 60　　　(k) 60　　　(l) 3600

B2 (a) s, min, h　　(b) l, cl, ml
(c) km, m, cm, mm　(d) kg, g

p 45

Now try this!
Second, minute, hour, day, week, fortnight, month, year, decade, century, millennium

p 46

A
(a) 0.48 m	(b) 1.37 m
(c) 5.4 cm	(d) 12.5 cm
(e) 1.4 km	(f) 1.76 km
(g) 5.362 km	(h) 0.467 km
(i) 62 cm	(j) 130 cm
(k) 39 mm	(l) 132 mm
(m) 1500 m	(n) 1530 m
(o) 3312 m	(p) 470 m

B
(a) 1.2 kg	(b) 1.64 kg
(c) 4.362 kg	(d) 0.866 kg
(e) 3500 g	(f) 5330 g
(g) 1584 g	(h) 567 g
(i) 1.647 l	(j) 5.3 l
(k) 58 ml	(l) 9 ml
(m) 16 670 ml	(n) 673.2 cl

p 47

C
(a) 6.34 km = 6340 m
(b) 2.45 m = 245 cm
(c) 3.8 cm = 38 mm
(d) 27.5 m = 2750 cm
(e) 25.4 cm = 254 mm
(f) 2.482 km = 2482 m
(g) 75.8 m = 7580 cm
(h) 42.9 cm = 429 mm
(i) 5.8 m = 5800 mm

p 48

A1
(a) 100 m
(b) 1 g
(c) 500 cm^2
(d) 120 mm
(e) 350 l
(f) 400 km
(g) 200 g
(h) $\frac{3}{4}$ l
Sadie Hansa wins the quiz.

B E, F, B, A, C, D

p 49

C1
(a) 3.93 m
(b) 15.4 kg
(c) 160 ml
(d) 15 kg
(e) 1.4 l
(f) 3.2 kg
(g) 1.6 kg

p 50

A1
(a) 78.8 kg
(b) 6
(c) 4
(d) 50
(e) 404.6 cm
(f) 82 cm
(g) 12
(h) 27.44 m
(i) 12.5 g

A2 EQUATIONS

B (a) 60   (b) 80   (c) 35   (d) 39   (e) 17

p 51

C1
(a) 38 cm	(b) 56 cm
(c) 74 cm	(d) 92 cm
(e) 6	(f) 8
(g) 11	(h) 14

C2 (a) 480 cm^2 (b) 160 cm

C3 (a) 400 cm^2 (b) 112.8 cm

p 52

A Angles are estimates.
(a) right
   90°
(b) acute
   60°
(c) obtuse
   110°
(d) obtuse
   150°
(e) acute
   30°
(f) straight
   180°
(g) reflex
   310°
(h) reflex
   350°
(i) reflex
   210°
(j) reflex
   270°
(k) reflex
   300°
(l) reflex
   220°
(m) obtuse
   140°
(n) reflex
   330°
(o) acute
   45°

p 54

A
(a) 6 cm^2	(b) 6 cm^2	(c) 4 cm^2	(d) 3 cm^2
(e) 3 cm^2	(f) 4 cm^2	(g) 2 cm^2	(h) $3\frac{1}{2}$ cm^2

p 56

A (a) Perimeter = 26 cm
Area = 40 cm^2

(b) Perimeter = 22 cm
Area = 28 cm^2

(c) Perimeter = 18 cm
Area = 18 cm^2

(d) Perimeter = 24 cm
Area = 35 cm^2

(e) Perimeter = 26 cm
Area = 30 cm^2

(f) Perimeter = 28 cm
Area = 45 cm^2

(g) Perimeter = 40 cm
Area = 96 cm^2

(h) Perimeter = 44 cm
Area = 121 cm^2

(i) Perimeter = 46 cm
Area = 90 cm^2

B1 (a) 90 cm^2
45 cm^2

(b) 160 cm^2
80 cm^2

(c) 81 cm^2
40.5 cm^2

(d) 120 cm^2
60 cm^2

(e) 84 cm^2
42 cm^2

(f) 156 cm^2
78 cm^2

B2 $A = \frac{1}{2} \times b \times h$

p 57

C1 (a) 69 cm^2 (b) 94 cm^2 (c) 92 cm^2
(d) 38 cm^2 (e) 87 cm^2 (f) 142 cm^2
(g) 202 cm^2 (h) 210 cm^2

C2 (a) 209 m^2 (b) 156 m^2 (c) 117 m^2
(d) 120 m^2 (e) 56 m^2

p 58

A1 (a) 6   (b) 24   (c) 54   (d) 96

A2 (a) 32   (b) 52   (c) 80
(d) 62   (e) 78   (f) 76

p 59

C2 (a) 56 cm^2 (b) 56 cm^2 (c) 58 cm^2 (d) 60 cm^2
(e) 60 cm^2 (f) 60 cm^2 (g) 62 cm^2 (h) 62 cm^2

Now try this!
(a) 280 cm^2
(b) 306 cm^2
(c) 364 cm^2